H E A T H
MIDDLE LEVEL
LITERATURE

Try, Try Again

It's not always easy, but nothing is impossible if you give it your best. Persistence pays off—sometimes in surprising ways.

A U T H O R S

Donna Alvermann
Linda Miller Cleary
Kenneth Donelson
Donald Gallo
Alice Haskins
J. Howard Johnston
John Lounsbury
Alleen Pace Nilsen
Robert Pavlik
Jewell Parker Rhodes
Alberto Alvaro Ríos
Sandra Schurr
Lyndon Searfoss
Julia Thomason
Max Thompson
Carl Zon

HEATH D.C. Heath and Company
Lexington, Massachusetts / Toronto, Ontario

STAFF CREDITS

EDITORIAL	Barbara A. Brennan, Marjorie Glazer, Christopher Johnson, Peg McNary, Lalia Nuzzolo, Rita M. Sullivan
	Proofreading: JoAnne B. Sgroi
CONTRIBUTING WRITERS	Carol Domblewski, Lisa Moore
SERIES DESIGN	Robin Herr
BOOK DESIGN	Caroline Bowden, Daniel Derdula, Susan Geer, Diana Maloney, Angela Sciaraffa, Bonnie Chayes Yousefian
	Art Editing: Carolyn Langley
PHOTOGRAPHY	*Series Photography Coordinator:* Carmen Johnson
	Photo Research Supervisor: Martha Friedman
	Photo Researchers: Wendy Enright, Po-yee McKenna, PhotoSearch, Inc., Gillian Speeth, Denise Theodores
	Assignment Photography Coordinators: Susan Doheny, Gayna Hoffman, Shawna Johnston
COMPUTER PREPRESS	Ricki Pappo, Kathy Meisl, Richard Curran, Michele Locatelli
PERMISSIONS	Dorothy B. McLeod
PRODUCTION	Patrick Connolly

Cover Photograph: © David Young-Wolff/PhotoEdit. **Cover Design:** Caroline Bowden

Published simultaneously in Canada

Printed in the United States of America

International Standard Book Number: 0-669-32097-8

1 2 3 4 5 6 7 8 9 10-RRD- 99 98 97 96 95 94

Middle Level Authors

Donna Alvermann, University of Georgia
Alice Haskins, Howard County Public Schools, Maryland
J. Howard Johnston, University of South Florida
John Lounsbury, Georgia College
Sandra Schurr, University of South Florida
Julia Thomason, Appalachian State University
Max Thompson, Appalachian State University
Carl Zon, California Assessment Collaborative

Literature and Language Arts Authors

Linda Miller Cleary, University of Minnesota
Kenneth Donelson, Arizona State University
Donald Gallo, Central Connecticut State University
Alleen Pace Nilsen, Arizona State University
Robert Pavlik, Cardinal Stritch College, Milwaukee
Jewell Parker Rhodes, California State University, Northridge
Alberto Alvaro Ríos, Arizona State University
Lyndon Searfoss, Arizona State University

Teacher Consultants

Suzanne Aubin, Patapsco Middle School, Ellicott City, Maryland
Judy Baxter, Newport News Public Schools, Newport News, Virginia
Saundra Bryn, Director of Research and Development, El Mirage, Arizona
Lorraine Gerhart, Elmbrook Middle School, Elm Grove, Wisconsin
Kathy Tuchman Glass, Burlingame Intermediate School, Burlingame, California
Lucretia Pannozzo, John Jay Middle School, Katonah, New York
Carol Schultz, Jerling Junior High, Orland Park, Illinois
Jeanne Siebenman, Grand Canyon University, Phoenix, Arizona
Gail Thompson, Garey High School, Pomona, California
Rufus Thompson, Grace Yokley School, Ontario, California
Tom Tufts, Conniston Middle School, West Palm Beach, Florida
Edna Turner, Harpers Choice Middle School, Columbia, Maryland
C. Anne Webb, Buerkle Junior High School, St. Louis, Missouri
Geri Yaccino, Thompson Junior High School, St. Charles, Illinois

CONTENTS

THE LITERATURE

Lise Martin Silverman

ASKING BIG QUESTIONS ABOUT THE LITERATURE

PROJECTS

1 WRITING WORKSHOP

HOW TO . . . STEPS TO SUCCESS 106-111

What can you do well? Break the process into steps. Then give a demonstration to your classmates.

2 COOPERATIVE LEARNING

DAY ONE AT A NEW SCHOOL 112-113

What should every fifth grader know for success at middle school? Prepare a booklet of advice.

3 HELPING YOUR COMMUNITY

EVERYONE HAS SKILLS FOR SUCCESS 114-115

Everyone enjoys the feeling of success. Plan games and prizes that give all children a chance to be recognized.

If at first you don't succeed, . . .

Success or failure—why do some people succeed when others fail? Often the answer is that they persist. They keep on trying. Successful people keep trying until they accomplish what they set out to do. Another key to success is teamwork. When people help one another, an "impossible" task becomes possible.

Have you ever thought you could create a musical instrument and then play a tune? Your answer may be, "No, that's impossible." In this activity, however, you'll work with a partner or a group to accomplish what, at first, might seem impossible. In this musical challenge, you'll make an instrument and play music—any pleasant sound or series of sounds made with an instrument.

1 Make an instrument.

With your partner or group, decide what instrument you'll make based on things already in the classroom or school yard. Here are some ways to make music.

KEYS TO SUCCESS

Keep the goal in mind.

Be flexible, accept change.

Listen to others.

Decide and act.

Keep trying.

Enjoy the process.

- Blow across the top of a bottle.
- Fill glasses with different levels of water. They make sounds with different pitches when struck.
- Across a box or ruler, stretch rubber bands to be strummed or plucked.
- Strike a hollow or solid object with a stick to make a drum. A book and a pencil will do.
- Shake a jar or box containing small, loose objects like paper clips.

Work on your instrument until you can make several different sounds that you can repeat.

₂ Choose a tune.

With your partner or group, decide on a tune to play. Choose a simple tune, something most people can recognize, like "Three Blind Mice," "Row, Row, Row Your Boat," or "Twinkle, Twinkle Little Star." Or you might compose your own tune.

₃ Practice and perform the tune.

No matter which tune you choose, remember that the goal is to make music. Practice until it's agreed that you're ready. Perform your tune and then become the audience for others. As you listen, think about how each group met its goal.

₄ How did you do it?

You just made music! How did you do it? You set goals and worked together to accomplish them. As a group, discuss the effort you put into making an instrument. Did you succeed the first time you tried? Did you have to keep changing the design of the instrument or the materials to get sounds you liked? How did you help one another succeed? Did each group face similar problems? Share your thoughts with the rest of your class.

Asking Big Questions About the Theme

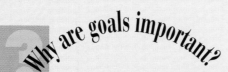

Why are goals important?

In your journal, write one-sentence answers to these questions. What do you want to learn to do this year? What other states would you like to visit before you leave high school? What job or profession will you aim for after school? Your answers can become your goals. Read your answers aloud. Do they seem more important when you hear them? Choose one goal of your own to write about in your journal. In a paragraph, tell how you could accomplish your goal.

What does it mean to succeed?

Success means different things in different situations. If you're a goalie, stopping a score is success. If you're a forward, success means you've scored. In your journal, draw a chart like this one. In the first column, list each role you play in life. In the second column, name one way you're already a success in that role and then name something you'll do in the future to succeed.

WAYS TO SUCCEED	
Student	• pass a test
	• get an A in math
Friend	• write letters
	•
Teammate	• work hard at practice
	•

? Why is it important to persist?

Many of the things you do each day you take for granted. *For granted* means you feel as if you've always known how to do them. In your journal, make a list of the things you do now that you couldn't do when you were three years old. If you hadn't persisted, how many items on your list would be missing? Don't forget reading and writing, tying your shoes, and whistling!

? How can people support others?

In the dictionary, there are more than seven meanings for the word *support*. *Help* and *pay for* are just two. Think about the people who have supported you in your life. In your journal, make a support pyramid like the one shown here. Put yourself at the very top. Name each of your supporters in the other boxes. Include their jobs if you don't know their full names. Don't forget your teachers. They have helped you become who you are.

NOW Think!

What goals have you set for yourself? With hard work and the support of others, you're sure to succeed. As you read *Try, Try Again*, you'll meet a number of individuals who never gave up. Think about what you can learn about success from each one of them.

THE MARBLE CHAMP

Lupe Medrano,[1] a shy
girl who spoke in whispers,
was the school's spelling bee
champion, winner of the reading
contest at the public library three sum-
mers in a row, blue ribbon awardee in the science fair, the top student at her piano recital,
and the playground grand champion in chess. She
was a straight-A student and—not counting kindergarten, when she had been stung by a wasp—never missed
one day of elementary school. She had received a small trophy
for this honor and had been congratulated by the mayor.

GARY SOTO

But though Lupe had a razor-sharp mind, she could not make her
body, no matter how much she tried, run as fast as the other girls. She
begged her body to move faster, but could never beat
anyone in the fifty-yard dash.

1. **Lupe Medrano** [lü′ pā me drä′ nō]

The truth was that Lupe was no good in sports. She could not catch a pop-up or figure out in which direction to kick the soccer ball. One time she kicked the ball at her own goal and scored a point for the other team. She was no good at baseball or basketball either, and even had a hard time making a hula hoop stay on her hips.

It wasn't until last year, when she was eleven years old, that she learned how to ride a bike. And even then she had to use training wheels. She could walk in the swimming pool but couldn't swim, and chanced roller skating only when her father held her hand.

"I'll never be good at sports," she fumed one rainy day as she lay on her bed gazing at the shelf her father had made to hold her awards. "I wish I could win something, anything, even marbles."

At the word "marbles," she sat up. "That's it. Maybe I could be good at playing marbles." She hopped out of bed and rummaged through the closet until she found a can full of her brother's marbles. She poured the rich glass treasure on her bed and picked five of the most beautiful marbles.

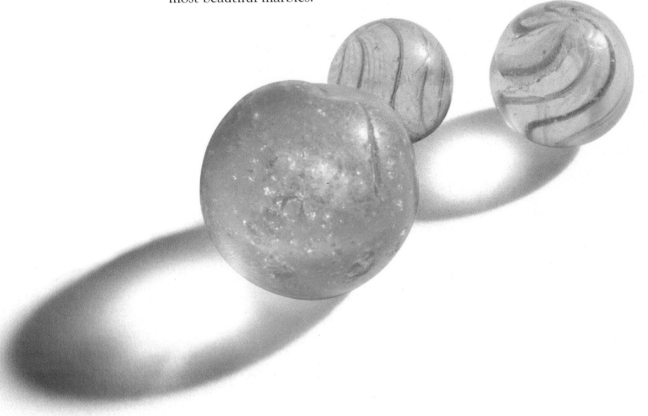

She smoothed her bedspread and practiced shooting, softly at first so that her aim would be accurate. The marble rolled from her thumb and clicked against the targeted marble. But the target wouldn't budge. She tried again and again. Her aim became accurate, but the power from her thumb made the marble move only an inch or two. Then she realized that the bedspread was slowing the marbles. She also had to admit that her thumb was weaker than the neck of a newborn chick.

She looked out the window. The rain was letting up, but the ground was too muddy to play. She sat cross-legged on the bed, rolling her five marbles between her palms. Yes, she thought, I could play marbles, and marbles is a sport. At that moment she realized that she had only two weeks to practice. The playground championship, the same one her brother had entered the previous year, was coming up. She had a lot to do.

To strengthen her wrists, she decided to do twenty push-ups on her fingertips, five at a time. "One, two, three . . ." she groaned. By the end of the first set she was breathing hard, and her muscles burned from exhaustion.[2] She did one more set and decided that was enough push-ups for the first day.

She squeezed a rubber eraser one hundred times, hoping it would strengthen her thumb. This seemed to work because the next day her thumb was sore. She could hardly hold a marble in her hand, let alone send it flying with power. So Lupe rested that day and listened to her brother, who gave her tips on how to shoot: get low, aim with one eye, and place one knuckle on the ground.

"Think 'eye and thumb'—and let it rip!" he said.

After school the next day she left her homework in her backpack and practiced three hours straight, taking time only to eat a candy bar for energy. With a popsicle stick, she drew an odd-shaped circle and tossed in four marbles. She used her shooter, a milky agate[3] with hypnotic[4] swirls, to blast them. Her thumb *had* become stronger.

---

2. **exhaustion** [eg zôs′ chən]: a state of being very tired or worn out.
3. **agate** [ag′ it]: a marble that looks like agate, a mineral with colored stripes running through it.
4. **hypnotic** [hip not′ ik]: seeming to be able to cast a spell or hypnotize.

After practice, she squeezed the eraser for an hour. She ate dinner with her left hand to spare her shooting hand and said nothing to her parents about her dreams of athletic glory.

Practice, practice, practice. Squeeze, squeeze, squeeze. Lupe got better and beat her brother and Alfonso,[5] a neighbor kid who was supposed to be a champ.

"Man, she's bad!" Alfonso said. "She can beat the other girls for sure. I think."

The weeks passed quickly. Lupe worked so hard that one day, while she was drying dishes, her mother asked why her thumb was swollen.

"It's muscle," Lupe explained. "I've been practicing for the marbles championship."

"You, honey?" Her mother knew Lupe was no good at sports.

"Yeah. I beat Alfonso, and he's pretty good."

That night, over dinner, Mrs. Medrano said, "Honey, you should see Lupe's thumb."

"Huh?" Mr. Medrano said, wiping his mouth and looking at his daughter.

"Show your father."

"Do I have to?" an embarrassed Lupe asked.

"Go on, show your father."

Reluctantly,[6] Lupe raised her hand and flexed her thumb. You could see the muscle.

The father put down his fork and asked, "What happened?"

"Dad, I've been working out. I've been squeezing an eraser."

"Why?"

"I'm going to enter the marbles championship."

Her father looked at her mother and then back
"When is it, honey?"

"This Saturday. Can you come?"

5. **Alfonso** [əl fon′ sō]
6. **reluctantly** [ri luk′ tənt lē]: unwillingly.

The father had been planning to play racquetball with a friend Saturday, but he said he would be there. He knew his daughter thought she was no good at sports and he wanted to encourage her. He even rigged some lights in the backyard so she could practice after dark. He squatted with one knee on the ground, entranced by the sight of his daughter easily beating her brother.

The day of the championship began with a cold blustery[7] sky. The sun was a silvery light behind slate clouds.

"I hope it clears up," her father said, rubbing his hands together as he returned from getting the newspaper. They ate breakfast, paced nervously around the house waiting for 10:00 to arrive, and walked the two blocks to the playground (though Mr. Medrano wanted to drive so Lupe wouldn't get tired). She signed up and was assigned her first match on baseball diamond number three.

Lupe, walking between her brother and her father, shook from the cold, not nerves. She took off her mittens, and everyone stared at her thumb. Someone asked, "How can you play with a broken thumb?" Lupe smiled and said nothing.

7. **blustery** [blus′ tər ē]: stormy.

She beat her first opponent easily, and felt sorry for the girl because she didn't have anyone to cheer for her. Except for her sack of marbles, she was all alone. Lupe invited the girl, whose name was Rachel, to stay with them. She smiled and said, "OK." The four of them walked to a card table in the middle of the outfield, where Lupe was assigned another opponent.

She also beat this girl, a fifth-grader named Yolanda, and asked her to join their group. They proceeded to more matches and more wins, and soon there was a crowd of people following Lupe to the finals to play a girl in a baseball cap. This girl seemed dead serious. She never even looked at Lupe.

"I don't know, Dad, she looks tough."

Rachel hugged Lupe and said, "Go get her."

"You can do it," her father encouraged. "Just think of the marbles, not the girl, and let your thumb do the work."

The other girl broke first and earned one marble. She missed her next shot, and Lupe, one eye closed, her thumb quivering with energy, blasted two marbles out of the circle but missed her next shot. Her opponent earned two more before missing. She stamped her foot and said "Shoot!" The score was three to two in favor of Miss Baseball Cap.

The referee stopped the game. "Back up, please, give them room," he shouted. Onlookers had gathered too tightly around the players.

Lupe then earned three marbles and was set to get her fourth when a gust of wind blew dust in her eyes and she missed badly. Her opponent quickly scored two marbles, tying the game, and moved ahead six to five on a lucky shot. Then she missed, and Lupe, whose eyes felt scratchy when she blinked, relied on instinct and thumb muscle to score the tying point. It was now six to six, with only three marbles left. Lupe blew her nose and studied the angles. She dropped to one knee, steadied her hand, and shot so hard she cracked two marbles from the circle. She was the winner!

"I did it!" Lupe said under her breath. She rose from her knees, which hurt from bending all day, and hugged her father. He hugged her back and smiled.

Everyone clapped, except Miss Baseball Cap, who made a face and stared at the ground. Lupe told her she was a great player, and they shook hands. A newspaper photographer took pictures of the two girls standing shoulder-to-shoulder, with Lupe holding the bigger trophy.

Lupe then played the winner of the boys' division, and after a poor start beat him eleven to four. She blasted the marbles, shattering one into sparkling slivers of glass. Her opponent looked on glumly as Lupe did what she did best—win!

The head referee and the President of the Fresno Marble Association stood with Lupe as she displayed her trophies for the newspaper photographer. Lupe shook hands with everyone, including a dog who had come over to see what the commotion[8] was all about.

8. **commotion** [kə mō′ shən]: a disturbance, tumult.

That night, the family went out for pizza and set the two trophies on the table for everyone in the restaurant to see. People came up to congratulate Lupe, and she felt a little embarrassed, but her father said the trophies belonged there.

Back home, in the privacy of her bedroom, she placed the trophies on her shelf and was happy. She had always earned honors because of her brains, but winning in sports was a new experience. She thanked her tired thumb. "You did it, thumb. You made me champion." As its reward, Lupe went to the bathroom, filled the bathroom sink with warm water, and let her thumb swim and splash as it pleased. Then she climbed into bed and drifted into a hard-won sleep.

GARY SOTO

Gary Soto was born in 1952 in Fresno, California. He grew up in a close family in a lively neighborhood of Mexican Americans. Soto did not find his family's lack of money a major problem. Like some of the characters in Soto's stories, he picked grapes to help earn extra money for family needs.

Soto became known as a writer in his twenties—first for poems straight from his childhood memories, later for short stories as well. Not all of his heroes are winners, like the main character in "The Marble Champ." In another story from his book *Baseball in April,* the hero, Gilbert, takes karate lessons. Gilbert does not become another Bruce Lee, yet he learns some things worth knowing.

GARRETT A. MORGAN

GLENNETTE TILLEY TURNER

Everyone who has ever crossed a street safely with the help of a traffic light can thank Garrett A. Morgan. He is the inventor who thought of a way for people and cars to take turns crossing at intersections.

Garrett A. Morgan was born in Paris, Tennessee, on March 4, 1875. His parents, Sydney and Elizabeth Reed Morgan, had ten other children. Times were hard and at age fourteen Morgan struck out on his own—heading for nearby Cincinnati, Ohio. He found a job as a handyman.[1]

1. **handyman:** a person who does odd jobs.

Four years later he moved to Cleveland, Ohio. He arrived with only a quarter to his name, but he had a talent for fixing mechanical things—and for saving his money. He got a job as a sewing machine adjuster at the Roots and McBride Company. Before long he had thought of an idea. It was a belt fastener for sewing machines.

Garrett Morgan soon saved enough money to buy his own sewing machine business and purchase a home. His father had died by that time and he invited his mother to move to Cleveland. A year later he married Mary Anne Hassek. They enjoyed a long, happy marriage and were the parents of three sons.

Morgan was a good businessman. Before long he was able to open a tailoring shop in which he hired thirty-two employees. His shop made suits, dresses, and coats with sewing equipment he had built.

Although planning was important to his success, his next business venture came about by accident. He was trying to find a liquid chemical that he could use to polish sewing machines. While he was experimenting, his wife called him to dinner. Hurriedly, he wiped his hands on a pony-fur cloth on his workbench and the wiry fur hairs straightened out. Curious to see how this liquid would affect other kinds of hair, he tried it out on the Airedale dog[2] next door. The dog's hair got so straight that his owner hardly recognized him. After a bit more experimenting, Morgan put the chemical on the market as a product to straighten hair.

His next invention was a safety hood or "breathing device." In more recent years it has been called a gas mask. Morgan received a patent[3] for it (U.S. Patent No. 1,113,675) and as he stated: "The object of the invention is to provide a portable attachment which will enable a fireman to enter a house filled with thick suffocating gases and smoke and to breathe freely for sometime

2. **Airedale dog** [er′ dā l]: a large terrier with a wiry brown coat with dark markings.
3. **patent** [pat′ nt]: a government document that gives a person or company sole rights to make, use, or sell a new invention for a certain number of years.

therein, and thereby enable him to perform his duties of saving life and valuables without danger to himself from suffocation."

The safety hood won a first prize gold medal from the International Exposition for Sanitation and Safety.[4] The judges at the exposition immediately recognized its value. Morgan wanted to market his invention, but he believed prejudice[5] would limit his sales if his racial identity was generally known. He knew that some fire departments would rather endanger their firemen's lives than do business with a black inventor. He attempted to solve this problem in a most unusual way. He formed the National Safety Device Company. He was the only nonwhite officer. The other officers—one of whom had been the director of public works for the city of Cleveland—would arrange for demonstrations of the device and set up a canvas tent in the demonstration area. They would set a fire in the tent with an awful-smelling fuel made of tar, sulphur, formaldehyde[6] and manure. Once the fire was roaring, Morgan

4. **International Exposition for Sanitation and Safety:** a public event that brings together different nations and focuses on practical health and safety measures.
5. **prejudice** [prej′ ə dis]: an opinion formed without judging fairly, sometimes based on a single feature such as race.
6. **formaldehyde** [fôr mal′ də hīd]: a colorless gas with a sharp odor, used in water to preserve or disinfect.

would appear disguised as an Indian chief. He'd put on the gas mask and go in and remain up to twenty minutes while he extinguished[7] the flames. He would come out as good as new. This might have gone on indefinitely, but the night of July 25, 1916, changed everything. Morgan became a hero overnight.

That night there was a violent explosion at the Cleveland Waterworks. Approximately thirty workmen were trapped in a tunnel five miles out and more than 225 feet beneath Lake Erie.[8] Smoke, natural gases, and debris[9] kept would-be rescuers from entering the tunnel where the workmen were trapped. Family and friends didn't know whether anyone had survived the blast.

Finally, someone at the site of this disaster remembered that Garrett Morgan had invented a gas mask. It was about two o'clock in the morning when Morgan was called in. He, his brother Frank, and two volunteers put on gas masks and entered the tunnel. They were able to save the surviving workmen, including the superintendent, whom Morgan revived with artificial respiration.[10]

Newspaper wire services picked up the story. The account of Morgan's heroism appeared in papers across the country. This turned out to be a mixed blessing. The city of Cleveland awarded Morgan a diamond-studded gold medal for heroism. Safety hoods or gas masks were ordered by the U.S. government. Many American, English, and German veterans of World War I owe their lives to the gas masks. Chemists, engineers, and other people working with noxious fumes could work more safely. At first, many fire departments ordered gas masks for use in their work, but because of racial prejudice, the number of orders dwindled, and some orders were cancelled when it became known that Morgan was a black man. Meanwhile, Thomas A. Farrell, Cleveland's Director of Public Utilities,[11] wrote to the Carnegie Hero Fund Commission to inform them of Morgan's heroic deed. The Commission had been

7. **extinguished** [ek sting′ gwishd]: put out.
8. **Lake Erie** [ir′ ē]: the fourth largest of the five Great Lakes.
9. **debris** [də brē′]: ruins, rubbish.
10. **artificial respiration:** a means of restoring normal breathing to a person who has stopped breathing by forcing air into and out of the lungs.
11. **Public Utilities:** essential public services, such as electricity, water, or train or bus transportation.

endowed by Andrew Carnegie to reward people who had shown great heroism. Instead of awarding Garrett Morgan, the Commission gave the hero medal to the project superintendent whose life Morgan had saved. People who knew that Morgan deserved this honor realized this was very unfair.

Instead of being discouraged, Garrett Morgan went back to his drawing board. Without the disappointment of the gas mask, he might never have developed his next invention, the stoplight. While the gas mask saved the lives of people who did dangerous work, the traffic light has saved the lives of drivers and pedestrians—of all ages, all across the world.

Reportedly, Morgan was the first black person in Cleveland to own a car. As the number of cars increased, there was a need for an effective[12] way to control the flow of traffic. Intersections were especially dangerous. Morgan put his problem-solving skills to work and invented the three-way automatic electric stoplight. It didn't look like today's stoplight, but it provided the concept on which modern stoplights are based. For some time, railroads had used a semaphore or signaling system.

Train engineers could look straight down the track and tell from the position of the semaphore whether to stop or proceed. Since city streets intersect, Morgan had to come up with a way to signal drivers on side streets as well as main thoroughfares. He received his patent (U.S. Patent No. 1,475,024) on November 20, 1923. At first, Morgan marketed the invention himself, but then decided to sell rights to the General Electric Company for $40,000. He not only had quite a lot more money than he had when he arrived in Cleveland— he had made two gigantic contributions to public safety.

Even though Garrett Morgan's contributions made life easier for everyone, regardless of race, he had been the victim of racism. Believing that no one should be denied opportunities because of their race, he worked to try to keep other people from having the kind of bad experiences he had had. He went about solving this problem in several different ways. He was concerned that the local newspapers didn't contain much news about the black community and things that were being accomplished there, so he started the *Cleveland Call* newspaper. (It is now known as the *Call and Post* and has

---

12. **effective** [ə fek′ tiv]: producing the desired results.

a large circulation.[13]) He was active in civil rights organizations.[14] And feeling that black citizens were not properly represented in local government, he ran for City Council. Although he did not win that election, Cleveland later became the first large American city to elect a black man as mayor.

For the last twenty years of his life, Morgan suffered from glaucoma.[15] This resulted in near-blindness, but it didn't slow down his sharp mind. Although he had hoped to attend the Emancipation Centennial[16] to be held in Chicago in August, 1963, Garrett Morgan died less than a month before that event. But he had lived to receive a well-deserved honor. Six months before his death he was cited[17] by the United States government for having invented the first traffic signal.

13. **circulation** [sėr′ kyə lā′ shən]: the number of copies of a newspaper or magazine sent out during a certain time period.
14. **civil rights organizations:** groups concerned with protecting the private rights of citizens and with laws protecting those rights.
15. **glaucoma** [glô kō′ mə]: an eye disease that causes gradual loss of sight.
16. **Emancipation Centennial:** the anniversary celebration marking one hundred years since the slaves were set free in the United States.
17. **cited** [sīt′ əd]: referred to, given credit for.

GLENNETTE TILLEY TURNER

Glennette Tilley Turner was born in 1933 in Raleigh, North Carolina. She grew up with a real interest in the way people have faced challenges and overcome obstacles. As a child, this interest led her to read biographies of people with courage. As an adult, Turner became an elementary school teacher. After twenty-five years as a teacher, Turner retired to become a full-time writer.

Much of Turner's writing is her favorite kind of reading—biographies. "Garrett A. Morgan" is one of the short biographies in her book *Take a Walk in Their Shoes.* She has also written a biography of Lewis Latimer, a little-known African American poet and inventor who grew up in Boston before the Civil War.

Turner has written articles for magazines like *Scholastic, Scope,* and *Ebony, Jr.* She is also the author of a book about the underground railroad in DuPage County, Illinois.

from Nadja on My Way

NADJA SALERNO-SONNENBERG

From the day I signed up for the Naumburg Competition,[1] everything changed. I had made a decision to start again, to save my life, and that meant a 360-degree turnaround.

I immersed myself in practicing. An enormous amount of work had to be done in two months. I went from not practicing at all to thirteen hours a day.

My fingers were like linguine.[2] I spent two weeks just playing scales. If I thought I sounded bad before, now I sounded worse than awful.

At the time I lived on 72nd Street, close to West End Avenue. I had an efficiency apartment with a window the size of a shoebox. I didn't do my laundry, I left my apartment only to walk to Juilliard[3]— and not on Broadway like everyone else. I walked up Amsterdam Avenue because I didn't want to see anybody, didn't want to bump into anybody, didn't want anyone to ask what I was doing.

I stopped going to classes and became a hermit. I even talked Miss DeLay into giving my lesson at night.

My eating habits were awful. I lived on fried sausages, a pint of peanut butter/chocolate ice cream, and a gallon of Coca-Cola every day. That's all I ate for eight weeks.

I was nuts. I was completely obsessed with getting back into shape, with doing well in this competition. If I could, people would know I was still on earth. Not to count me out; to stop asking, "Whatever happened to Nadja?"

The last week before the Naumburg auditions, I couldn't touch the violin. I had worked and worked and worked and worked and then I just couldn't work anymore.

I certainly could have used it. I wasn't as prepared as I should have been. But I simply had to say, "Nadja, you've dedicated yourself to this thing. Ready or not, do your best."

---

1. **Naumburg Competition** [naùm búrg]: the violin competition named after a city in East Germany.
2. **linguine** [lin′ gwē nē]: thin, flat pasta.
3. **Juilliard** [jül′ ē ärd]: a leading school for the performing arts located in Manhattan.

Fifty violinists from around the world auditioned for the competition on May 25, 26, and 27, 1981. Those that made it past the preliminaries would go on to the semifinals. Those that passed that stage would go to the finals. In years past, one violinist was chosen as winner and two received second and third place.

On May 26, the day of my audition, I went to the Merkin Concert Hall at 67th Street and Broadway. I waited, played for twenty minutes, and went home. I couldn't tell whether the preliminary judges were impressed or not. I'd find out the next evening.

Maybe subconsciously[4] I was trying to keep busy; that night, when I fried the sausages, I accidentally set my apartment on fire. I grabbed my cat and my violin, and ran out the door. The fire was put out, but everything in my place was wrecked.

Fortunately, the phone was okay and on the evening of May 27, I had the news from Lucy Rowan Mann of Naumberg. Thirteen of us had made it.

Talk about mixed emotions. I was thrilled to be among the thirteen; a group that included established violinists, some of whom had already made records. But it also meant I had to play the next day in the semifinals of the competition.

Everyone entering the competition had been given two lists of concertos. One was a list of standard repertory[5] pieces. The other list was twentieth-century repertory. For our big competition piece, we were to choose from each list and play a movement from one in the semifinals, and a movement from the other in the finals—if we made it that far.

From the standard repertory list, I chose the Tchaikovsky Concerto.[6] I had been playing the Tchaik for three years, so it was a good piece for me.

4. **subconsciously** [sub kon′ shəs lē]: existing in the mind but not fully perceived or recognized.
5. **repertory** [rep′ ər tôr′ ē]: music an artist is prepared to perform.
6. **Tchaikovsky Concerto** [chī kôf′ skē kən cher′ tō]: a long musical piece for one or more principal instruments, such as a piano or violin, and an orchestra, by the Russian composer Peter Tchaikovsky in 1878.

From the twentieth-century list, I chose the Prokofiev G minor Concerto.[7] I had never played it onstage before.

My goal had been just passing the auditions, but now my thought pattern began to change. If I wanted a sliver of a chance of advancing again, my brain said, "Play your strong piece first."

Logically, I should play the Tchaikovsky in the semifinals just to make it to the next stage. Who cared if that left me with a piece I probably wouldn't play as well in the finals of the competition? It'd be a miracle to get that far.

7. **Prokofiev G minor Concerto** [prō kô′ fyef]: a piece of music identified by its key, written by Sergey Prokofiev, a nineteenth-century Russian composer.

There wouldn't be more than seven violinists chosen for the final round, and if I were in the top seven of an international group, that was plenty good enough.

The semifinals were held on May 28 in Merkin Concert Hall. You were to play for thirty minutes: your big piece first, then the judges would ask to hear another.

There was a panel of eight judges. They had a piece of paper with my choices of the Tchaikovsky and the Prokofiev in front of them. "Which would you like to play?" they asked.

I said meekly, "Prokofiev."

My brain and all the logic in the world had said play your strong piece. My heart said, "Go for it all. Play your weak piece now, save Tchaikovsky for the finals."

Maybe I don't listen to logic so easily after all.

My good friend, the pianist Sandra Rivers, had been chosen as accompanist[8] for the competition. She knew I was nervous. There had been a very short time to prepare; I was sure there'd be memory slips, that I'd blank out in the middle and the judges would throw me out. My hands were like ice.

The first eight measures of the Prokofiev don't have accompaniment. The violin starts the piece alone. So I started playing.

I got through the first movement and Sandra said later my face was white as snow. She said I was so tense, I was beyond shaking. Just a solid brick.

It was the best I'd ever played it. No memory slips at all. Technically, musically, it was there.

I finished it thinking, "Have I sold my soul for this? Is the devil going to visit me at midnight? How come it went so well?"

I didn't know why, but often I do my best under the worst of circumstances. I don't know if it's guts or a determination not to disappoint people. Who knows what it is, but it came through for me, and I thank God for that.

---

8. **accompanist** [ə kum′ pə nist]: a person who plays a musical part that helps or enhances the main part.

As the first movement ended, the judges said, "Thank you." Then they asked for the *Carmen Fantasy*.[9]

I turned and asked Sandy for an A, to retune, and later she said the blood was just rushing back into my face.

I whispered, "Sandy, I made it. I did it."

"Yeah," she whispered back, kiddingly, "too bad you didn't screw up. Maybe next time."

At that point I didn't care if I did make the finals because I had played the Prokofiev so well. I was so proud of myself for coming through.

I needed a shot in the arm; that afternoon I got evicted.[10] While I was at Merkin, my moped[11] had blown up. For my landlord, that was the last straw.

What good news. I was completely broke and didn't have the next month's rent anyway. The landlord wanted me out that day. I said, "Please, can I have two days? I might get into the finals, can I please go through this first?"

I talked him into it, and got back to my place in time for the phone call. "Congratulations, Nadja," they said. "You have made the finals."

I had achieved the ridiculously unlikely, and I had saved my best piece. Yet part of me was sorry. I wanted it to be over already. In the three days from the preliminaries to the semifinals, I lost eight pounds. I was so tired of the pressure.

There was a fellow who advanced to the finals with me, an old, good friend since Pre-College. Competition against friends is inevitable in music, but I never saw competition push a friendship out the window so quickly. By the day of the finals, I hated him and he hated me. Pressure was that intense.

The finals were held on May 29 at Carnegie Hall[12] and open to the public. I was the fourth violinist of the morning, then there was a lunch break, and three more violinists in the afternoon.

---

9. **Carmen Fantasy:** a violin and orchestra composition adapted by the Spanish composer Pablo de Sarasate from the 1875 opera *Carmen* by Georges Bizet.
10. **evicted** [i vikt′ əd]: expelled by law from a building.
11. **moped** [mō′ pəd]: a motorbike which can be pedalled as a bicycle or operated with a motor at up to 30 miles per hour.
12. **Carnegie Hall** [kär′ nə gē]: a world famous concert hall in New York City.

I played my Tchaikovsky, Saint-Saëns's *Havanaise*,[13] and Ravel's *Tzigane*[14] for the judges: managers, famous violinists, teachers, and critics. I went on stage at five past eleven and finished at noon. Those fifty-five minutes seemed like three days.

I was so relieved when I finished playing; I was finished! It's impossible to say how happy I was to see the dressing room. I destroyed my gown tearing it off, changed, and went out for lunch with my friends.

13. **Saint-Saëns's *Havanaise*** [saN-säNz ä vä näz′]: a piece written by the French pianist, Charles-Camille Saint-Saëns (1835-1921).
14. **Ravel's *Tzigane*** [rə′ velz tzē gen′]: a 1924 piece written by Maurice Ravel, a French composer.

It was like coming back from the grave. We laughed and joked and I got caught up on *General Hospital*.[15] I was calm but thrilled it was over. I made it to the finals, that's it, I'm done.

As I returned to Carnegie Hall to hear the other violinists, I realized I'd made a big mistake: they might ask for recalls. A recall is when they can't decide between two people and they want you to play again. It's been done; it's done all the time in competitions. No way was I in shape to go onstage and play again.

In the late afternoon, the competition was over. Everybody had finished playing. Quite luckily—no recalls.

The judges deliberated[16] for an hour. The tension in the air was unbelievable. All the violinists were sitting with their little circle of friends. I had my few friends around me, but no one was saying much now.

Finally, the Naumburg Foundation president—founder and first violinist[17] of the Juilliard String Quartet and that year's presenter—Robert Mann came on stage.

"It's always so difficult to choose . . ." he began.

Every year we hold this competition," Robert Mann said. "And in the past, we've awarded three prizes. This year we've elected to only have one prize, the first prize."

My heart sank. Nothing for me. Not even Miss Congeniality.[18]

"We have found," Mann went on, "that second place usually brings great dismay to the artist because they feel like a loser. We don't want anyone here to feel like a loser. Every finalist will receive five hundred dollars except the winner, who will receive three thousand dollars."

15. *General Hospital:* a popular long-running television soap opera.
16. **deliberated** [di lib′ ə rāt′ əd]: thought over carefully.
17. **first violinist:** a position of importance in an orchestra or smaller musical group, second only to the conductor.
18. **congeniality** [kən jē nē al′ ət ē]: quality of being most friendly or pleasant to be with.

And then he repeated how difficult it was to choose, how well everyone had played . . . dah, dah, dah.

I was looking down at the floor.

"The winner is . . ."

And he said my name.

A friend next to me said, "Nadja, I think you won!"

I went numb. My friends pulled me up and pointed me toward the stage. It was a long walk because I had slipped into a seat in the back.

Sitting up in front was my old friend. I would have to walk right past him and I was dreading it, but before I could, he got up and stopped me.

He threw his arms around me and I threw my arms around him. I kept telling him how sorry I was. I was holding him and started to cry, saying, "I'm sorry, I'm sorry, I'm sorry." I didn't want to lose, but I really didn't want him to lose either. And he was holding me and saying, "Don't be sorry. I'm so proud of you." It was over, and we would be friends again.

I took my bow, then ran to Juilliard. Ten blocks uptown, one block west, to give Miss DeLay the news. She could be proud of me now, too.

Suddenly, everything was clear. Playing the violin is what I'd do with my life. Heaven handed me a prize: "You've been through a lot, kid. Here's an international competition."

Everything had changed when I prepared for the Naumburg, and now everything changed again. I bought a gown at Saks[19] that cost as much as a season ticket at Yankee Stadium[20] (I kept thinking I could find something as good for five dollars at a garage sale). I made my first recording—Fauré[21] and Prokofiev sonatas with Sandra Rivers on the Musicmasters label. Between September 1981 and May 1982, I played a hundred concerts in America, made one trip to Europe, then two months of summer festivals. And people asked me back.

19. **Saks:** a department store whose name is known nationwide.
20 . **Yankee Stadium:** the place where the New York Yankees play baseball.
21. **Fauré** [fo rā´]: an influential French composer (1845-1925).

There was a great deal of anxiety playing in Europe for the first time. American musicians have their nationality to overcome. When you play Beethoven[22] in Germany, no matter what, they're going to hate you. The audience has come to hear the American violinist who dares to play Beethoven.

My first time in Germany, walking onstage and feeling the vibes, I would rather have been a fire hydrant on Broadway. But I was able to rely on my self-confidence to pull me through.

Self-confidence onstage doesn't mean a lack of nerves backstage. The stakes had increased. This wasn't practice anymore, this was my life. I'd stare into a dressing-room mirror and say, "Nadja, people have bought tickets, hired baby-sitters, you've got to calm down; go out there and prove yourself."

Every night I'd prove myself again. My life work had truly begun.

22. **Beethoven** [bā′ tō vən]: a well-known German composer (1770-1827).

N A D J A   S A L E R N O - S O N N E N B E R G

Nadja Salerno-Sonnenberg was born in Rome into a very musical family. Everyone played an instrument—including her grandmother who played the kazoo. Young Nadja herself started studying the violin very early.

In 1969, she came to the United States with her family on the liner *Michelangelo*. Once here, she learned English as fast as possible and became a Yankees fan just as rapidly. The family settled in Cherry Hill, New Jersey, and Salerno-Sonnenberg continued her studies. Her education has not been limited to music, however. She believes in learning from everything—including galleries, museums, radio, and videos. She never stops studying, practicing, and learning. "Some days I can't believe I've come as far as I have," she says, "and how much further I have to go."

HAYES IVERSON
(BASKETBALL STAR)

MEL GLENN

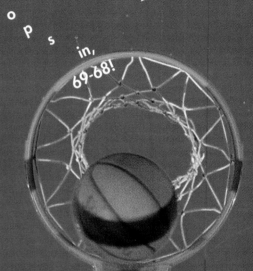

The score is tied,
Hands smooth with sweat,
God, let the ball
Fall through the net.
I'm on the line,   5
Shooting a pair,
First one rolls off,
Black-hole despair.
Ball feels heavy,
Bounce it once more,   10
Slow breath—let it
Drop for the score.
The ball is up,
Universe waits,   15
The ball
                    d
                     r
                      o
                       p
                        s   20
                         in,
                    69-68!

LANCE PERKINS
(FOOTBALL STAR)

MEL GLENN

G	If	
5	I	
10	run	
15	this	
20	punt[1]	5
25	back	
30	for	
35	a	
40	touchdown,[2]	
45	do	10
50	you	
45	promise	
40	me	
35	that	
30	the	15
25	cheering	
20	and	
15	applause	
10	will	
5	never	20
G	stop?	

1. **punt:** the kick of a dropped football before it touches the ground.
2. **touchdown:** the score of six points made in football by putting the ball on the ground behind the opponent's goal line.

MEL GLENN
....

Mel Glenn, the son of American citizens, was born in 1943 in Zurich, Switzerland, yet he grew up in Brooklyn, New York. Like the rest of his neighborhood, he was a big sports fan and he played basketball in the park "until it was too dark to see the hoop."

Besides a love of sports, Glenn knew one thing—he was going to be a writer. "At New York University, Glenn followed both paths by covering sports events for the college newspaper. He expected to be a journalist. When President Kennedy was assassinated, however, Glenn joined the Peace Corps, becoming an English teacher in West Africa.

His work now covers all that Glenn likes best: writing, sports, and teaching. The subjects of his poems are the students he teaches, many of whom are active in sports. These poems are found in *Class Dismissed* and *Class Dismissed II: More High School Poems*. Glenn also writes novels for young people.

A Very Special

Fighting Machine

Brent Ashabranner

The Ed Parker Karate[1] Studio in Pasadena, California, has a tranquil[2] Oriental look on the outside. Inside, it is cramped and the few pieces of furniture well worn and a bit shabby, but on the walls are photographs of famous Hollywood personalities who have worked out or trained at the studio, including Bruce Lee.[3] On our first visit, the studio was full of noise with the arrival of young people for a workout session.

We had come for that session, but first we went to the office of Frank Trejo,[4] manager of the studio. Frank is a big man, too big for his small, cluttered office. The office walls were filled with diplomas showing his progress in karate. He is sixth level Black Belt, which puts him near the top of the karate discipline.

1. **karate** [kä rä′ tē]: a Japanese means of self-defense and fighting without weapons.
2. **tranquil** [trang′ kwəl]: peaceful, calm.
3. **Bruce Lee:** an American movie star of Asian descent whose first movie in the 1970s made martial arts and body-building popular.
4. **Frank Trejo** [trā′ hō]

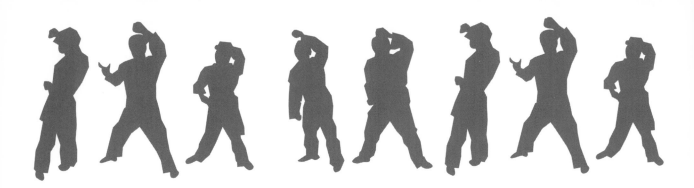

Trophies he had won in national and international competition were scattered around the office, including some on the floor.

"I'm a mean, mean fighting machine," he said, with a smile.

We were at the studio because two weeks earlier I had seen Frank on the NBC "Today Show" drilling a group of severely handicapped students in karate exercise. It had been an impressive sight, and I wanted to see it for myself. Now, in the short time before the workout, I wanted to dig into Frank's background and learn how he came to be a professional in karate. Frank is outgoing, talks easily and fast. All I had to do was ask a couple of questions and then keep quiet and listen.

Frank comes from a Mexican-American family. He grew up in Pasadena, but his mother and father were migrant[5] farm workers. "We were poor, my whole family," he said. "I'm still poor. My grandfather and uncle were boxers during the Depression.[6] Me and my brother didn't have much choice but to fight, too. I was a real skinny, lanky kid, but by fourteen I was a pretty good little fighter. Karate always fascinated me. There was something mystical about it. The first time I came into this place, I knew this was going to be my life."

I asked about the Ed Parker studio. Ed Parker, I was told, was one of the legendary figures in karate; there are Ed Parker studios all over the country.

"When I was sixteen," Frank continued, "I got a job at a car wash so that I could give my brother karate lessons. Then I would

5. **migrant** [mī′ grənt]: moving from one place to settle in another.
6. **Depression** [di presh′ ən]: a period of very low economic activity in the 1930s.

learn all the moves from him. I would say, 'How does that go?' And we'd go over and over all the moves. In '69 I answered an Ed Parker newspaper ad for instructors. I got the job! They taught me, and I taught beginners. 'This is the block. This is the punch. This is the kick.' Man, I taught that stuff ten hours a day. But along the way I became a teacher, a real teacher."

Just then one of Frank's helpers came to the door to say that the class was ready, and we went into the workout room. About twenty boys and girls were there, dressed in white karate workout uniforms. All this group was from Lincoln School in the nearby town of San Gabriel. I knew from talking earlier to Jan Taylor, a psychologist at the school, that all were students in the special education program, severely handicapped in some way. Some had Down's syndrome[7] with differing degrees of mental retardation; others had cerebral palsy[8] with speech, hearing, and muscular control problems and in some cases mental retardation; still others were autistic,[9] with special learning and movement problems. This was one of eight special groups from different schools that worked out with Frank during the week—130 students in all.

I also knew that many physical therapists, physical education specialists, and medical experts were skeptical[10] and pessimistic[11]

7. **Down's syndrome:** a condition present from birth characterized by limited mental development.
8. **cerebral palsy** [sər′ ə brəl päl′ zē]: a paralysis caused by damage to the brain.
9. **autistic** [ô tis′ tik]: demonstrating limited development in communication skills.
10. **skeptical** [skep′ tə kəl]: inclined to doubt.
11. **pessimistic** [pes′ ə mis′ tik]: inclined to see all the difficulties.

that young persons with such severe handicaps could learn activities that called for the exercise of memory and group coordination.

And then I watched Frank Trejo in action. With the help of two assistants, he got the group of students into rows. They began with the traditional bow of respect to the instructor. After that Frank took them through a series of karate warm-up exercises: neck rotations, hip and waist rotations and bending, leg stretches and squats, and other loosening-up maneuvers. After that they practiced the "horse," a stability stance in which the legs are set about twice as far apart as shoulder width. They practiced blocks, punches, and hand movements, all designed to develop upper body dexterity.[12]

Frank, in his black workout uniform, his voice loud as he called out instructions, was like a magnet for the students' attention. They followed his every move and did their best to imitate. What was most obvious of all was that they were thoroughly enjoying what they were doing and enjoying being a part of this activity together. Frank was patient but insistent that they do the exercises correctly. The assistants worked with individuals, and from time to time Frank would give one of the students his individual attention.

Jan Taylor was there from Lincoln School, as were some teachers from other schools that had groups training with Frank. I talked with them and found they were all convinced that the karate program was helping the young participants in many ways: improved motor skills, longer attention span, improved ability to follow instructions, more stamina[13] and strength.

"And a better feeling about themselves, an improved self-image," Jan said. "That may be most important of all."

Later, when the students had returned to school and the studio was quiet, I settled down with Frank again. "How did this start?" I asked him. "What made you think you could teach karate to boys and girls like the ones who were just here?"

12. **dexterity** [dek ster′ ə tē]: skill in using the body and hands.
13. **stamina** [stam′ ə nə]: endurance.

The idea didn't start with him, Frank said, but rather with Lauren Tewes, the actress who for years was one of the stars of the "Love Boat" television series in the role of the cruise director. "She was one of my karate students," he said, "and she also worked with handicapped children in the Very Special Arts Festival that is held in Los Angeles every year. It's kind of like the Special Olympics for handicapped kids, but it focuses on singing, painting, dancing, things like that.

"Lauren got the idea that maybe I could train a group of handicapped kids to perform karate in the Very Special Arts Festival. I had my doubts. I was really skeptical. And then I started hearing people saying it couldn't be done. Well, I had a learning disorder when I was in school. I didn't know how to read. Oh, I could read the words, but I couldn't put them together to make sense. I finally taught myself how to read six years ago.

"And in 1983, I got a broken neck from a blow to the head in a karate tournament. I was paralyzed on my right side. Surgery fixed that, but I had to build myself back up through karate exercises.

"So I figured I knew something about the problems these kids have. And I didn't like people saying no one could teach them karate skills. I figured, I'm a teacher. I can try. But then the first tryout was arranged, on the baseball field at Pasadena High School, and I stood out there in front of those kids, and I said to myself, what have I got myself into now? But by the end of that first session I could see that they could learn and wanted to learn and liked it, and I started working with them twice a week. We worked for about five months, and then we put on a program in the Very Special Arts Festival. I'm told it was a big success."

It was, in fact, a huge success and led to the program that is now going on in the eight schools. Frank has worked hard

to find and develop those special features of karate that are most appropriate for severely handicapped young people. The program has been given the name Creative Physical Fitness, and it is attracting nationwide attention.

I knew that Frank had given all of his time to the program on a volunteer basis. "You may become rich and famous," I said.

"I'm still poor," he said again.

BRENT ASHABRANNER

Brent Ashabranner was born in 1921 in Shawnee, Oklahoma. He started out as a young reader fascinated by stories of adventure in foreign places. As an eleven-year-old boy, he started writing a novel called *Barbara the Jungle Girl.* "That wasn't very original," he says, because he had just finished reading *Bomba the Jungle Boy.* He never got past page three. "But that was a start," he says, "and I never stopped writing after that."

Ashabranner joined the Peace Corps and began nonfiction writing at the same time. "The things I felt I was learning seemed worth sharing with young readers." He has gone on to write more books about social issues.

For Ashabranner, the challenge of writing about problems in society is "to make these subjects interesting and understandable." Among Ashabranner's many books are *People Who Make a Difference* and *Always to Remember: The Story of the Vietnam Veterans Memorial.*

A Very Special Fighting Machine   **45**

The Confidence Game

PAT CARR

My confidence started draining out my toes the day Angela Brady showed up at the pool for workout. I even started to chew the inside of my cheek, a nervous habit I usually reserve for fighting the fear that clutches at me just before a race. In a way, I guess I knew it *was* a race between Angela and me for the backstroke position on our team relay for National Championship.

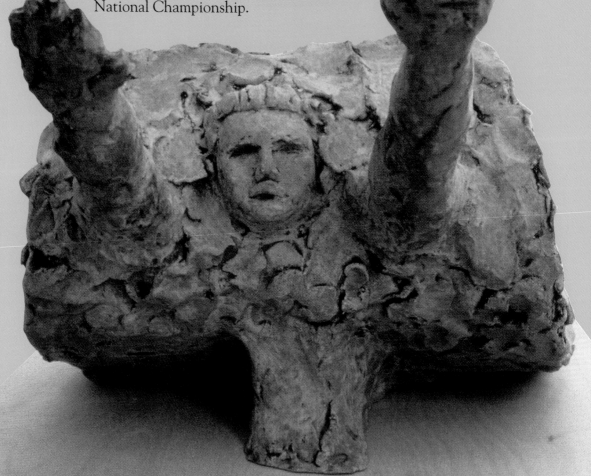

Georgia Martin Silverman, 1978, 32" high, edition of 4

I hadn't even seen her swim yet, but the whole team knew she had been swimming for a famous club in California. We were just a small city team, only two years old. But we had a coach whose middle name was motivation.[1] He'd motivated me into swimming a grueling[2] three miles a day, and now I was actually in the running to compete at the Nationals. Or I was until Angela showed up.

"Okay, swim freaks, hit the water for an 800 meter freestyle warm-up!" barked Coach. Then he added in a more human voice, "Angela, why don't you try lane four today?"

Lane four was the fast lane, my lane. I'd had to earn my place in that lane by swimming 400 meters in less than five minutes. Now all Angela had to do was jump in. It wasn't fair.

I didn't think I could pretend friendliness, so I started the 800 before Angela hit the water. But I didn't even have time to settle into my pace when I felt the water agitating[3] behind me. I stroked harder, but I could still feel the churning water of someone closing in on me. I soon felt a light touch on my foot.

In swim workouts, it's one of the rules that when a teammate taps your foot you move to the right to let that swimmer go ahead of you. I knew that, and I also knew that I was interfering with Angela's pace by not letting her pass me. My conscience[4] told me to move over, but something stubborn kept my body in the middle of the lane.

At the end of the 800, I glanced up and saw Coach staring at me. Realizing that he had seen me refuse to let Angela pass, I took a deep breath and ducked underwater.

When the workout was over, everyone crowded around Angela, asking her if she knew any Olympic swimmers and stuff like that. Finding a quiet corner for myself, I slipped on my warm-up suit, draped a towel over my head and hurried toward my bike.

"Hey, Tobi! Where are you going?" someone shouted.

---

1. **motivation** [mō′ tə vā′ shən]: the reason or encouragement to act.
2. **grueling** [grü′ ə ling]: very tiring.
3. **agitating** [aj′ ə tāt′ ing]: moving violently.
4. **conscience** [kon′ shəns]: sense of right and wrong.

I didn't answer, just hopped on my bike and pedalled fast.

It was like that for the next two weeks. At every workout Angela was the star of the show; I was an invisible stagehand. Even worse, during time trials she beat me in all four strokes and took my place as lane leader.

I was miserable. And I was scared, too; scared that Angela was taking away my chance at the Nationals, a chance I had earned by a lot of hard work.

I started to show up late to workouts so that I wouldn't have to talk to anyone. I even walked on the bottom of the pool and faked my stroke, a swimmer's cheating trick I'd never used before. It was easy to catch up to Angela that way. And I always managed to be underwater when she gave our lane instructions.

I'll admit I wasn't very happy with my actions. But my jealous feelings were like a current I couldn't swim against.

The day before the Riverdale Meet, Coach called me over. At that moment I would rather have tried to talk to King Kong.

"Tobi, I want to talk to you about sportsmanship," he began.

5. **quipped** [kwipd]: spoke cleverly.

"Sportswomanship, in this case, Coach," I quipped,[5] hoping to distract him.

"Okay, sportswomanship," he said, taking me seriously. "Or whatever you want to call it when one athlete accepts a better athlete in a spirit of friendly competition."

"Maybe the so-called better athlete is not as good as everyone thinks," I mumbled.

Coach left a big silence for my statement to fall into. I started to chew the inside of my cheek again.

"Let's stop talking about this athlete and that athlete," he said softly, "and talk instead about Tobi and Angela. She has made better time than you, Tobi. And that is an objective fact, not something everyone thinks."

He paused. I stared at my toes, which were curling under my feet as if trying to hide.

"The worst of it, Tobi, is that your attitude is hurting your performance. Do you know that your times have become worse in the last two weeks? Maybe showing up late and walking on the bottom have something to do with that," he said. My face felt as if it had been splashed with hot pink paint.

"Do you have anything you want to say?" he asked. I shook my head. "That's all then, Tobi. I'll see you tomorrow at the Riverdale Meet."

The next morning I was too nervous to eat my special breakfast of steak and eggs. This meet would decide who was going to Nationals.

The early skies were still gray when I arrived at the Riverdale pool for the warm-up session. The other swimmers were screeching greetings at each other like a flock of gulls. I jumped into the water to cut off the sound and mechanically[6] began my stroke.

Half an hour later, I shuddered as the public address system squealed. The meet was about to start. After climbing out of the pool, I quickly searched the heat sheet[7] for my name. Disappointed, I saw that I had just missed making it into the last, and fastest, qualifying heat.[8] Angela's name, of course, was there. She'd taken my place just as she had at the trials.

Better not to think about Angela at all, I told myself, recalling Coach's words. Better to concentrate on my own race. Carefully, I went over Coach's instructions in my mind, shutting out the milling[9] crowd around me, swimming my race perfectly, over and over again in my head, always perfectly.

"Would you like an orange?"

Without looking I knew whose voice it was. "It's good for quick energy," continued Angela, holding the orange out to me.

"No thanks," I said. "I've got all I need." I saw that she was about to sit down next to me, so I added, "I don't like to talk before a race."

She nodded sympathetically. "I get uptight, too. The butterflies are free," she said with a nervous laugh.

For a moment I felt a little better toward her, knowing that she had the jitters, too. Then I remembered that she didn't have to worry.

"You'll be an easy winner," I said.

"You never know," she replied uncertainly.

6. **mechanically** [mə kan′ ə kəl ē]: automatically.
7. **heat sheet:** a list of athletes competing in the heats, or trials before a race.
8. **qualifying heat** [kwol′ ə fī ing]: early trial in which athletes that meet a required level of performance become eligible to compete in the next race.
9. **milling:** moving in a confused way.

My heat was called. Up on the blocks[10] I willed my muscles into obedience, alert for the starter's commands. At the gun, I cut into the top of the water smoothly.

I swam exactly as I had been imagining it before the race, acting out the pictures in my mind. I felt the water stream past me, smooth, steady and swift. When I finished, I was certain I had done my best in that heat.

Overwhelmed by exhaustion, I sat on the deck for several minutes, eyes closed, totally spent. I knew I was missing Angela's heat, but I was too tired to care.

The sound of the announcer's voice was like a crackling firecracker of hope bursting through my fatigue.[11] Then I heard my name. I'd made it!

I also heard Angela's name, but it was several minutes before I realized that my name had been called last. That meant my time had been better. Figuring there must have been a mistake I checked the official postings, but there were our times with mine four seconds faster.

Heading for the gym, where all the swimmers rest and wait for the heats to be called, I saw Angela sitting with her back against the wall alone. Her shoulders were rounded in a slump.

It could be me, I whispered to myself, remembering what it feels like to mess up a race. There's no worse anger than the kind you feel toward yourself when you've ruined something you care about. I knew how she felt, and I also knew there was no way I could make up for the way I had acted. But I just had to try.

"I don't talk before races, but I do talk after them. Sometimes it helps," I said, knowing Angela had

10. **blocks:** platforms on which racers stand at the start of a race.
11. **fatigue** [fə tēg′]: weariness from hard work.

Breaker Martin Silverman, 1978-1979, cast bronze, 40″ x 8″, edition of 3

every right to tell me to go drown myself.

"Talk if you want to," she murmured.[12]

"Well, I will, but I was hoping you'd talk, too."

She hesitated, and I saw her trying to swallow. "I will as soon as I'm sure I'm not going to cry," she whispered.

So I babbled on for a few minutes about the meet, some of the other swimmers, the team standings, anything. I knew it didn't matter what I said as long as I kept talking.

All at once, Angela interrupted my opinion of the snack bar's hamburgers. "I do this all the time," she burst out. "I do great at workouts, then comes a meet, and something happens; I just can't do it."

"Maybe you don't know how to play the confidence game," I said. She looked at me suspiciously, but I went on. "How do you psych yourself up for a race?"

"I don't exactly." She was twisting the ends of the towel into tiny corkscrews. "I just try to block it out, not think about it."

"What about during a race?"

"I concentrate on not making mistakes."

"Very negative methods," I commented.

"What do you mean?"

"Well, take my positive approach. First, I think about all the good things I've done in previous races. Then I plan my upcoming race carefully, going over each detail in my mind, picturing myself the perfect swimmer. Then when I'm in the water, I tell myself to do it again, only this time for real."

"And you win," Angela added with a smile. Now I really felt badly, remembering how I had acted when Angela had done better than I in workouts.

"Listen, I have an idea," I said. Maybe I *could* make it up to her. "You swim faster than me, right?" Angela looked doubtful.

"Yes, you do, that's an objective fact," I insisted. "Now my idea is that you use me as a pacer[13] in the backstroke final this afternoon."

At first Angela wasn't sure, but I soon had her convinced, and we were planning our strategy when Coach showed up.

12. **murmured** [mėr′ mərd]: said in a soft, low voice.
13. **pacer**: a person that sets an example of speed for others to keep up with.

"What's going on here?" He gave me an accusing look.

"We've got it all settled," Angela spoke up. "Tobi and I are going to be a team from now on."

"All right!" he said, giving us a smile usually reserved for winners.

As Angela and I sat together on the ready bench,[14] I had conflicting thoughts about helping her. What was I doing anyway? Handing her my relay position[15] on a silver platter, that's what.

I hadn't time to get worked up over it, though, because the whistle blew, and we stepped up to the blocks. At the sound of the gun I was into the water with barely a splash, skimming the surface like a water bug.

As I reached the wall, I pretended all my strength was in my legs as I flipped and pushed off. Pull hard, hard, hard, I told myself, muscles aching from the effort. Then on the last lap, I concentrated on a single word. Win! I shot through the water and strained for the finish.

Immediately, I looked to Angela's lane. She was there, but it was too close to tell who had won.

She gave me the thumbs up sign, and I returned it.

I stared at the electronic scoreboard. Usually it didn't take long for the times to appear, but now it remained blank for so long I was beginning to worry that a fuse had blown.

Please, please let me be the winner, I whispered over and over. Finally, the winning times flashed on. I blinked away the chlorine haze, or maybe tears. Angela had won. I managed to give her a congratulatory hug.

"I couldn't have done it without you, Tobi," she bubbled.

"You did it, girls!" Coach couldn't keep himself from shouting, he was so excited. "You've just raced yourself to the Nationals!"

I had never felt so left out, so disappointed in my whole life. "Well, at least Angela has," I said, struggling to smile.

Coach looked startled. "And you did, too, Tobi."

What was he talking about? "I saw that Angela won the place on our relay team."

"That's right, but you missed something. You both swam so fast

14. **ready bench:** a bench on which swimmers sit at the start of a race.
15. **relay position:** a specific distance a swimmer must complete in a race.

that you made qualifying times for the *individual* backstroke event!"

I was stunned. I had concentrated so hard on the relay place I hadn't even thought about the individual events.

"So you'll both go to the Nationals!" Coach couldn't resist doing a couple of dance steps, and I was so ecstatic, I joined him. But a wet concrete swim deck is not an ideal dance floor.

"Look out!" yelled Angela, as we just missed falling into the water. "I don't want my partner to break a leg. We've got a long way to go before the 1980 Olympics."

"What?" I gasped.

"Just doing some positive mental rehearsing," she grinned.

"A little confidence sure goes a long way," I retorted.

Still, maybe that *is* something to think about!

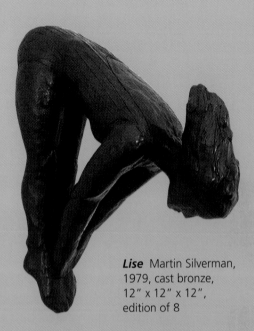

Lise Martin Silverman, 1979, cast bronze, 12″ x 12″ x 12″, edition of 8

PAT CARR

Pat Carr was born in 1932 in Grass Creek, Wyoming. She grew up there but went on to live in a number of interesting places. Carr considers that the years she lived in South America, Texas, and New Orleans "provided her favorite settings." But at the top of the list is her childhood in Wyoming. Carr feels very fortunate that her generation "has been able to experience a wide range of conflicts and emotions." Even though she is grateful for the particular history of her own generation, Carr has set many of her stories in the Civil War.

Both Carr and her husband have two careers. In addition to their writing, they both teach college. Pat Carr's books include novels, nonfiction, mythology, and short stories. "The Confidence Game" is from *Young Miss*.

Abstractions Robert Dillworth, 1979, graphite on paper, 24 $\frac{1}{2}$ x 34 $\frac{1}{2}$

NO CHILDREN HERE

A L E X   K O T L O W I T Z

Pharoah[1] would have liked Rickey to root him on at the school spelling bee, but his friend spent the period in the principal's office, where he sat out most assemblies. Ms. Barone had sent him there as a precaution, because, if he felt moved to, he could have disrupted[2] the entire proceedings. Lafayette[3] couldn't make it either, since the contest was only for the middle grades.

Pharoah prepared diligently[4] for the annual spring event, which pitted the school's top third-, fourth-, and fifth-graders against one another. A dozen students competed, two from each classroom. Ms. Barone had conducted her own class bee to choose two representatives. Pharoah was one; the other was a boy named Jimmy. Clarise,[5] the class's star pupil, was absent the day Ms. Barone chose the contestants.

1. **Pharoah** [fer′ ō]
2. **disrupted** [dis rupt′ əd]: broken up.
3. **Lafayette** [läf ā et′]
4. **diligently** [dil′ ə jənt lē]: in a hard-working manner.
5. **Clarise** [clə rēs′]

Pharoah wanted badly to do well, but he knew that to do so he'd have to control his stammer,[6] which had worsened with his family's troubles. He wanted to succeed at everything he took on. He liked to stand out. He relished the attention. And, he figured, if he tried hard enough, everything would work out okay. (He was just as hard on others as he was on himself. A loyal Chicago Cubs fan, Pharoah would berate players if they didn't get a hit in a critical situation. "Man," he'd say, "Andre Dawson didn't try hard enough.") He felt confident that he would at least place second or third in the spelling bee.

He established a routine for himself in which he'd first sound the word out in his head, pause a moment to remind himself to take his time, and then spell it, drawing out each letter slowly and deliberately so as not to stutter.[7] For over three weeks, he had studied fourteen mimeographed[8] sheets of words.

On the day of the competition, Ms. Barone asked the two young contestants to come to the head of the classroom. "We wish you lots of luck," she said to the two nervous boys. "I know you can do it. I know you can win. Remember the rules. You have to say the word. Spell it. And then say it again. Good luck." Their classmates applauded and on the way to the auditorium tugged at their arms and told them to do well.

Pharoah and the other eleven contestants lined up on the small wooden stage in the school's gymnasium, which doubled as an auditorium. They faced the judges, who sat to the side, so that their right shoulders were turned to the audience. Pharoah was bright, Ms. Barone thought. He'll do okay. He looked handsome in his freshly pressed turquoise[9] cotton shirt, buttoned at the collar. The name tag she'd printed for him stood out as she hoped it would. Made of bright yellow construction paper, it read PHAROAH RIVERS in huge block

6. **stammer** [stam′ ər]: hesitation in speaking.
7. **stutter** [stut′ ər]: repeat the same sound in an effort to speak.
8. **mimeographed** [mim′ ē ə grafd]: copied.
9. **turquoise** [tèr′ koiz]: sky-blue or greenish-blue.

letters. It looked weighty on his tiny frame; he was considerably shorter than the other contestants.

Pharoah was much more nervous than anyone knew. He was praying that he wouldn't stutter. If he did, people would laugh and make jokes. It would be humiliating. Not in front of all these people. Please. He started wringing his hands in apprehension.[10]

The head judge took the lecturn[11] and explained the rules, repeating Ms. Barone's instructions. Pharoah, though fidgety, listened attentively. There was a stool for those, like Pharoah, who couldn't reach the microphone. If a word sounded unfamiliar, the students could ask to hear it used in a sentence. Few, though, ever made that request. If a student misspelled a word, a buzzer would sound and he or she had to leave the stage.

Pharoah was so focused on controlling his speech and spelling the words right that he paid little attention to the other contestants. The first few rounds were a blur. All he remembers were words like *Catholic* and *abandonment, adjust,* and *Appalachian.*[12] He knew how to spell them all. As student after student walked off the stage in defeat, Pharoah realized he was getting closer and closer to winning. He spelled *kangaroo,* a word he knew but had never seen in print before. His classmates, who were asked to hold their applause, clapped their hands silently.

But as the contestants were whittled down to five, Pharoah's nerves began catching up with him. He could feel himself losing the self-control he'd fought so hard to retain. He had unconsciously[13] untucked his shirt. His hands balled up beneath it, playing with the fabric. His next turn came around quickly.

"*Endurance,*"[14] the teacher announced. "*Endurance.*"

Detail from **Abstractions**
Robert Dillworth

10. **apprehension** [ap´ ri hen´ shən]: fear, dread.
11. **lecturn** [lek´ tərn]: a stand used by a speaker to hold papers or a book.
12. **Appalachian** [ap ə lā´ chən]: referring to the region in the eastern United States, covering parts of eleven states from Pennsylvania to Alabama.
13. **unconsciously** [un kon´ shəs lē]: without being aware.
14. **endurance** [en dür´ əns]: the power to withstand hard wear.

Pharoah felt his heart pumping fast and loud. He knew how to spell the word. He knew, in fact, what it meant. He couldn't restrain his joy, and, abandoning his usual routine, he spoke in a rush, quicker than he should have. His eyes darted around excitedly.

He repeated the word. *"Endurance,"* he said, spitting out the three syllables as if they were one. He then started to spell it: "E-N-D-U . . ." He couldn't hear a thing. Nothing came out of his mouth. Nothing. He tried again. Nothing. His stutter, which had got-

Detail from
Abstractions
Robert Dillworth

ten worse in recent months, devoured him. The letters knotted up in his throat; the veins in his neck strained as he tried to get them out. The buzzer sounded. Pharoah's lips quivered in disappointment. He did all he could to keep from crying in front of his friends.

When he went to sit down with his class to watch the rest of the bee, Ms. Barone put her arm around him and pulled him to her. "You did a good job, Pharoah," she told him. "We're proud of you."

When Pharoah got home from school that day, he walked straight back to his room. LaJoe, who was at the sink washing dishes, knew something must be wrong; he always greeted her. She went back to see him. He was lying on his bed.

"How'd you do today, Pharoah?" she asked. He told her. LaJoe assured him there was nothing to be ashamed of. "It's going to be all right. You okay in my book." She tried to soothe him, stroking his head. "I love you. You can spell for me whenever you get ready to." He had tried his hardest.

"Pharoah is Pharoah. He's going to be something," she would tell friends. "When he was a baby, I held him up and asked him if he'd be the one. I've always wanted to see one of my kids graduate from high school. I asked him if he'd be the one to get me a diploma."

But for Pharoah that wasn't good enough. He knew how to spell better than most kids his age. He should have won, or at least placed second. He was just going to have to work harder. Pharoah promised his mother he'd do better next year. Pharoah was not one to break his word.

ALEX KOTLOWITZ

Alex Kotlowitz writes about urban affairs and social issues for the *Wall Street Journal.* Before joining the staff at that newspaper, Kotlowitz wrote as a freelance journalist for National Public Radio. He also writes articles for magazines.

Kotlowitz visited the Chicago project where this story takes place in 1983. He had gone there to do research for an essay he was writing to go along with a friend's photographs. Lafayette was in one of the pictures, and Kotlowitz met the boy and his family at that time. Two years later, Kotlowitz spent the summer visiting the same project for a newspaper story he was writing about the effects of violence on children's lives. He became good friends with both Lafayette and his younger brother Pharoah, and the friendship lasted.

In 1988, Kotlowitz asked the boys' mother about writing a book that would tell what children's lives were like in the neighborhood. According to Kotlowitz, the mother thought it was a good idea but, she said, "There are no children here." This, she said, was because they had seen too much to be children. From her words, Kotlowitz found the title for a book that follows the boys for two years of their lives. Kotlowitz has continued to be their friend. Their story has not ended.

BUSTING

JOHN GROSSMANN

If you play sports, you know how much fun they can be. You know the thrill of competing. You know how challenging it is to try to become faster, stronger, and more skilled.

Now imagine if you couldn't play sports. No matter how much you wanted to play, people would say that you don't fit in or that sports are too dangerous for you. You could only sit and watch.

That's how kids with physical and mental disabilities used to be treated. No one gave them a chance to race, throw, bat, ski, shoot baskets, or take part in other sports activities. They missed out on all the fun.

Fortunately, times have changed. Thanks to organizations such as the Special Olympics, National Handicapped Sports, and the National Wheelchair Athletic Association, kids with disabilities are finally getting a chance to play—and they're doing great!

Three disabled kids who have really been digging into sports lately are Sarah Billmeier[1], Joe Manriquez[2], and Jennifer Hazen. They are among the most amazing kid athletes you'll ever read about.

1. **Sarah Billmeier** [sa′ rə bil′ mi ər]
2. **Joe Manriquez** [män re′ kez]

LOOSE!

Sarah uses outrigger ski poles to help balance herself as she cuts around a slalom gate.

Sarah Billmeier, 14

When she was 5 years old, Sarah learned she had bone cancer. To save her life, doctors had to amputate her left leg and remove her left hip.

Sarah didn't let that stop her from playing sports—lots of them. Today, she is a sports-minded freshman at Yarmouth High School in Yarmouth, Maine. She competes for an age-group swim team, plays second base and outfield for her school softball team, and is a goalie for her school soccer team. She plays all of these sports on one leg. She doesn't even use crutches or an artificial leg.

Sarah's best sport is downhill skiing. She skis on one ski. She cuts back and forth between the gates, which are poles stuck into the snow, by shifting her weight. To help her keep her balance, she uses outriggers, special ski poles with short skis on the ends.

Sarah competes in slalom[3] and giant slalom events. She races for an able-bodied ski team in New Hampshire, and she competes across the country at meets for disabled skiers. In 1990, she won gold medals in four events in the junior division at the U.S. Disabled Ski Championships. This past April, Sarah moved up to the women's division, and she won two bronze medals.

Sarah was named to the U.S. Disabled Women's Ski Team this past spring. She is the only skier on the team younger than 20. Sarah hopes to compete at the Paralympics in Albertville, France, next March, and at the 1994 Winter Olympics, where disabled skiing will be a demonstration sport.

Sarah says she doesn't even remember what it felt like to have two legs. "For her, having one leg is normal," says her mother, Nancy. "She really doesn't see herself as disabled."

3. **slalom** [slä′ ləm]: a zigzag downhill skiing race.

Joe Manriquez, 14

Joe was born mentally retarded. That means a part of his brain does not function properly and so he learns more slowly than most kids.

Joe lives in San Antonio, Texas. He attends special classes at Terrell Wells Middle School, and he learns what are called life skills. These skills will allow him to take care of himself when he becomes an adult. He learns how to ride the bus, wash clothes at a Laundromat, do arithmetic on a calculator, and read signs that say STOP or DANGER.

Joe loves to watch sports on television, and his favorite team is the Miami Dolphins of the National Football League. Joe's most prized possession, though, is the black and gold jersey that he wears when he plays for the Harlandale school district basketball team. When Joe and his teammates were invited to a San Antonio Spurs practice last year, Joe had the jersey autographed by the Spurs' star center, David Robinson, and by the Spurs' mascot,[4] The Coyote.

4. **mascot** [mas′ kot]: an animal or symbol that supposedly brings good luck to a team.

Joe also competes in the Special Olympics, an international program for people who are mentally retarded. The Special Olympics holds competitions in a variety of sports, and Joe swims, runs track and field, bowls, and plays tennis, volleyball, and softball. However, his favorite sport to play is basketball. "Joe's working on a pretty good outside shot," says Tanya Huerta,[5] who coaches Joe's team.

"Sports have helped Joe gain tremendous self-confidence," says Tanya. "They give him a chance to have fun and be a kid, and yet they help him grow up. They're very positive for him."

(Note: Special Olympics meets are great fun. If you are interested in helping at one as a volunteer, write Volunteer Coordinator, Special Olympics International, 1350 New York Ave. NW, Suite 500, Washington, D.C. 20005.)

Jennifer Hazen, 13

Jennifer cannot walk, so she uses a wheelchair. But that doesn't slow her down one bit. She is a champion in both track and field and swimming.

Jennifer had an operation on her heart when she was 11 months old. Doctors believe the blood supply to her spinal cord was cut off during the operation. This damaged nerves in her spine and left Jennifer paralyzed. She cannot move her legs.

Jennifer is a freshman at Bloomfield High School in Bloomfield, New Jersey. She started using a wheelchair when she was 4, and a few months later she entered her first track-and-field meet. She competed against other boys and girls in wheelchairs, and she loved racing.

5. **Tanya Huerta** [tän′ yä wār′ tä]

Jennifer began swimming in 1990. She competes in backstroke, freestyle, and breaststroke events. She swims using only her arms, which are very strong from wheelchair racing.

Jennifer has competed in eight National Junior Wheelchair Championships in track and field. In 1990, competing against girls age 12 and younger, Jennifer won track races of 100, 200, 400, and 800 meters, and she finished third in the javelin throw, shot put, and discus throw.[6]

At the nationals this past July, Jennifer competed in the division for girls ages 13 to 15. She finished third in five track races and was third in the javelin, fifth in the shot put, and fourth in the discus.

Jennifer has set high goals for herself. "I want to make the U.S. Disabled Team," she says. "I want to compete in the 800-meter wheelchair event for disabled athletes at the 1996 Olympics."

6. **javelin throw, shot put, discus throw:** sporting events in which contestants throw a spear, a heavy metal ball, and a heavy wooden plate.

A Personal

Kim-Hue Phan

I was born in Saigon,[1] and I escaped from Vietnam[2] four years ago. I'm seventeen now and in the eleventh grade in an American school.

When I left home, Saigon was in bad shape; it was not pretty like it was before 1975. We didn't have a house in the city anymore. After the war[3] was over in 1975, we lived outside the city, and I was really lucky to stay in school. I usually got up about 5:00 A.M., cooked breakfast for the family, cleaned the house and went to school from 7:00 A.M. to noon. After school, I cooked lunch and cared for the family. I promised my parents to take care of all my younger brothers and sisters. If everything went okay, then I could stay in school. My father drove a bus to different cities; my mother went along with my father to buy merchandise to sell to the black market[4] in Saigon. My sister worked at a factory.

1. **Saigon** [sī′ gän]: the capital of South Vietnam.
2. **Vietnam** [vē et′ näm′]: a country in Southeast Asia. From 1957-1976, it was divided into North and South Vietnam.
3. **war**: the Vietnam War (1957-1975) was fought between South Vietnam, the United States, and their allies on one side and North Vietnam and their allies on the other side.
4. **black market**: a place where goods are sold at unlawful prices and quantities.

Narrative

School in Saigon was hard. Mostly we read books and took tests. Children had to memorize a long poem or essay every day. Most of the teachers were really mean; I was spanked because I couldn't memorize a poem. After 1975, the rule was that teachers should not punish the kids, but I was spanked again because I did not write a five-page essay about flowers in a basket. My father protested, and the teacher didn't spank me after that.

In seventh grade in Saigon, we had to read hero stories a lot. After 1975, the communists[5] took over the country and republished all our books. Their stories were about heroes who spied for the North Vietnamese.[6] We usually read a biography of Ho Chi Minh.[7] I used to go to the library to borrow the books. The communists didn't allow non-communist books in libraries. They allowed only books published by the communists, like hero stories or biographies of

5. **communists:** people who support communism, an economic system where most of the property is owned by the state as a whole. After the United States withdrew from Vietnam in 1975, the North Vietnamese Communists gained control of Vietnam.
6. **North Vietnamese:** the Communist forces of North Vietnam.
7. **Ho Chi Minh** [hō′ chē min′]: a Vietnamese leader of the Vietminh, the Communist group that gained power in northern Vietnam.

Viet Cong.[8] I was forced to read these communists' stories. Many people were against the communists but were afraid to say anything against them.

My parents wanted my brother Minh and me to have freedom and arranged for us to escape out of Vietnam to a free country. It was 1982, and I had just finished seventh grade. One morning at approximately 4:00 A.M., my parents told us to get out of bed. I was very sleepy, and I asked my father why we had to get up so early. He told me that my brother and I had to go away for a long time. Minh was glad that we were going on a trip because most of the time we never went anywhere except around the city. The early morning was cloudy and dreary, much like my feeling about leaving my family— probably forever. Our parents told us to act as natural as possible, so that neighbors and police would never suspect this was our great escape. Our parents had been planning this day for many months. Nothing could now interfere with the plans.

Our father took us to the bus station, which was the first part of our long trip to freedom. At about 5:30 A.M. that morning, my nine-year-old brother and I got off our father's motorcycle with just a small package that contained a change of clothing. We waited while our father bought the tickets. Then with my hat in hand, I boarded the old, light-colored bus. My brother looked for a seat for us, but I looked elsewhere. Outside, I saw my father near his motorcycle

8. **Viet Cong:** the Communist rebel force of South Vietnam, supporters of North Vietnam during the Vietnam War.

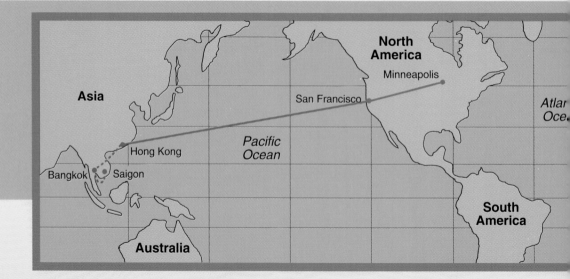

staring at the bus and his two children. I saw the sparkling in his eyes, and he tried to hide his feelings. I had never seen my father emotional before. I was thinking, "Dad, don't worry about us; we'll see you again, but I don't know when." His tall stature against the early morning light brought a sick feeling to my stomach. I tried so hard to hide my tears. So sadly, I took the seat. As the bus slowly moved on, my father grew smaller and smaller and smaller and finally disappeared. His gradual vanishing is a moment that I know I will never forget.

The next part of our journey was very hard. After waiting three days at a cottage near a beach, we were told to walk down to the river to a small fishing boat, which would take us to a larger boat. Twenty of us had to lie down while they put the fishing net over us. They pretended they were going out fishing so no one would know they were smuggling people out of the country. I was lying on the edge of the boat, trying to see my brother when I was almost pushed off into the water.

We finally reached the big boat but it was no better. It was hot and many people were seasick. I was glad my brother sat next to me so I could look after him. Suddenly the boat tipped, and a big wave washed over the side. Minh had a large burn on his left side from his shoulder to his waist. He was in pain from the salt water stinging his wound. At that moment, I wished I could have taken the pain away from him. After a day, we ran out of water and could have only half a cup twice a day. During that part of the journey, which lasted for three days and four nights, we didn't have any food. We finally

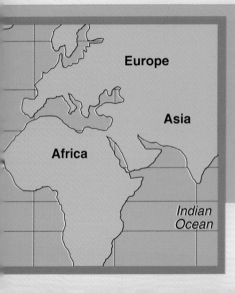

reached Thailand[9] where we stayed at the Children's Center, waiting to find a country with people to sponsor us.

After eight months in the camp, we were the last to go to America. We flew from Thailand to Hong Kong and then to California. From California we flew to Minneapolis, Minnesota.

When I first arrived in Minnesota, I remember running outside in my bare feet and getting a big surprise at the coldness of the snow. How different from the country which I had left! After I put on my shoes, I went for a walk alone. The trail of footprints in snow made me think of how different life was going to be. I looked at the snow on the ground, and the continual falling snow landed on my hand. Every flake had a different shape, a different design, a different size. I realized that I was not like the carefree snowflakes that flow to the ground without direction. I must stay here until a home was found for me. Suddenly I heard a car pass by. It made me jump and realize my mind was not fixed on any one thing. The fresh smell of air was such a change from my home country. I saw some blond, fair-skinned people loudly laughing behind me. They seemed like giants to me. I looked around for the familiar faces of friends or family, and deep loneliness came to me again. I felt like a deaf person when people spoke a greeting like "Hi" or "How are you?" because I did not understand what they were saying.

We stayed in Minneapolis for a month and mostly watched TV. I played basketball! Time was different so we slept a lot during the day. If we went for a walk during the day when nobody was home, my brother and I made marks in the snow so that we could get back. If we got lost, I couldn't speak English, so at the house, we drew a circle in the snow. Where we turned we made arrows. We didn't get lost.

During that time, our foster parents in another town were getting a room ready for us and clothes and personal needs. The social worker brought us to the town where we now live. It was kind of exciting and scary, too. You don't know how the family will treat you. I didn't know the words for *mom* or *mother* or *dad*. If I wanted to go to sleep, I had to point to the bed.

9. **Thailand** [tī′ land]: a country in Southeast Asia, a western neighbor of Laos and Cambodia. In the Vietnam War, Thailand was an ally of South Vietnam.

When we first came, we were so tired. We had to go to school every day and I slept in the classroom. At night I sat awake on my bed and played with toys. I was sleeping in class all the time. It took me about a month to get used to the time here.

In school I was like a deaf person. I walked into school in the morning, walked out of school in the afternoon and didn't understand what was going on that day. I went to school for three months without knowing English. I couldn't talk either. If I wanted to go to the bathroom, I looked in the dictionary for the word, wrote it down and showed it to the teacher. I felt like I was not smart enough to speak or understand. I thought I was a slow learner. My English started getting better. When I wrote a note to my foster mom I would put, "I go store." I looked at it again; my mind would say it isn't right. I corrected it, "I go to the store." I now have a "the" in there. That's how I started to do it. And I started reading more books. Mostly learning English taught my mind to think.

I kind of felt lonely at first. Nobody to talk to. Some of the kids tried to talk to me, but I couldn't talk back. Sometimes I went home and sat in my room and cried. My foster parents didn't know I was crying. I was trying so hard to speak with them. It was hard to do it. Sometimes I was getting depressed, and sometimes I was homesick for Vietnam. When I got used to it and started to speak English, I had more fun.

It's hard to pronounce r and l. We have r and l in the Vietnamese alphabet, but when we pronounce the words, we pronounce inside our throat—not too much with our tongue. We don't speak with our tongue. We never say the ends of words out loud. When I learned English, I forgot a lot of my Vietnamese for a long time. Now I have Vietnamese friends in high school to talk to, but I have a little accent in Vietnamese too. My brother, however, is so good. He speaks English perfectly. When you are younger, you have an easier time learning English.

At first in math class, I looked at the book and did the homework. I didn't understand what the teacher said. For a long time I thought "There is no test in USA!" I like school with no test. One day the math teacher gave me the test. I thought it was homework.

So I just did it slowly and took it home. The next day I came into the classroom and gave it to him. I thought he wanted to see homework. Now I think how dumb I was that first year of school in America.

When I first used magazines to write research papers, I had to translate with the dictionary word for word. About half of it I didn't understand. They used fancy words in there. I looked in the dictionary for the meaning. Sometimes I knew what the words meant, but not the sentences in the magazine. I had to ask someone what the sentence meant, and I put it in my own words for the meaning. It was hard; I was frustrated and tired. I had to take all the things I had wrong and rewrite and correct. The teacher wanted me to recopy many times. Sometimes I didn't want to do it. I struggled a lot.

I still write short. My paragraphs are not long. When the teacher wants me to write about three pages, I write only a page and a half. My mind tries to expand it, but I can't do it. I like to read, but writing is too hard. If I could talk better, I could write better. I want to be just like American kids. That would help me a lot. To be a good student in reading and writing, you have to practice every day. It's just like dancing. If you continue practicing dance, someday you'll be a dancer.

My foster mom is good in English. She knows what's going on— what's right, what's wrong. I learned from her. That's how I learned to write. Sometimes after I wrote a paragraph, she'd say, "Hey, this paragraph isn't right." "Yes, it's right," I'd say. And we'd sit there and go back and forth with the paragraph. Finally she'd say, "Well, you do whatever you want." Sometimes I would get mad. When I was mad, I wrote down everything, page after page. When I calmed down, I would throw the papers away. I appreciate what she did for me, though.

Sometimes I fell behind. Sometimes, I was way ahead of everyone. When I fell behind, I was way behind. My mind would not do the work. I couldn't force it. I didn't want to work. I didn't want to do anything. I wanted to sit around. Then I took a walk, played basketball, sat alone and daydreamed just so I could get a break. Then I came back and studied normally.

The hardest thing now for me is my vocabulary. I don't know enough words. Sometimes I have ideas but no words for my ideas. I have to put my ideas down in simple, children's words. I'm trying to use new words, but I still don't know how to make them fit in the sentences. I spend much more time on my writing than the other kids do. I put a verb in back and forth, look for missing letters like "s's." I'm not good at verbs like past tense, present tense, "is," and "are." It is hard, but I'm doing all right on my own now. My grades go up and down, up and down. I made the honor roll. When I make the honor roll, I'm in a good mood.

It's easier to write about something I know. When I wrote a paper about leaving my family, the teacher read it aloud. Everyone felt sad, and some girls cried. I didn't want to hear the paper again. I started crying. The girls were trying to reach out and comfort me. The boys said "Good paper, congratulations."

School is real important to me. I want to learn so I can use it for my future in college. Maybe someday I will do major accounting or physical therapy and go somewhere with warm weather. If Vietnam becomes a free country, I may want to go back there. I worry about my parents in Vietnam. I'm trying to get my parents over here. Someday when I finish my college and have a good job, I can bring my family over here. Vietnam is a communist country so I can't visit my parents. If we become citizens of the United States, we can go over there and visit our parents with no danger. In one more year I will be a citizen.

KIM-HUE PHAN

Kim-Hue Phan arrived in this country in 1982 after escaping from Vietnam with her young brother. She wrote this personal essay in 1986 when she was in the eleventh grade in a high school in Minnesota. After graduation, she attended college in the Midwest but interrupted her education to work for two years to help support her family in Vietnam. She returned to college and graduated in January 1994. She has become a U.S. citizen and hopes to enjoy a career as an accountant.

THE TUBETEIKA AFFAIR

VYTAUTE ZILINSKAITE

Dotas charged only a trifle[1] for his advice: one stamp. It could even be a used stamp. Money? Oh no, he wanted none of that. There had been a time when he had charged five kopecks,[2] but his parents had heard about it. So from then on he took only stamps.

The fame of the wise counsellor Dotas in 3B had long ago spread through the school; but after the tubeteika[3] affair was settled, thanks to his ingenuity,[4] it spread far beyond its walls.

But let us go back to the beginning.

Spring had come with a rush. The thin white curtains could not withstand the sun and it poured in through the large windows onto the children. Now, who could be dull or depressed on such a day? There was not a single sombre face, the mood was one of spring gaiety—except for Andrius.[5] He was obviously worried. During break he had hovered[6] around the class wiseacre,[7] evidently with a problem. But Dotas took no notice, played hard to get. So it was only after school was out and they were on their way home that he overtook Dotas in the street and their historic consultation took place.

1. **trifle** [trī′ fəl]: a small amount.
2. **kopecks** [kō′ peks]: coins used in the former Soviet Union.
3. **tubeteika** [tyub bē tā′ kər]
4. **ingenuity** [in′ jə nü′ ə tē]: cleverness.
5. **Andrius** [an drē′ əs]
6. **hovered** [huv′ ərd]: stayed nearby.
7. **wiseacre** [wī′ zā′ kər]: a smart aleck.

Man's tubeteika, courtesy of Julia Babushkina

The fifteen independent states that formerly made up the Soviet Union

"Dotas! Wait for me!" Andrius called. "If you can't help me I'm done for!"

The trouble was this. Andrius's father had recently returned from Kirghizia[8]—so far off, that if you went there by train it would take four whole days! But Andrius's father had flown. It was quite different from Lithuania[9] there, he said, all

8. **Kirghizia** [kirʹ gē zē ə]: an independent nation (prior to December 1991, a part of the former Soviet Union), now called Kyrgystan.
9. **Lithuania** [lithʹ ə wāʹ nē ə]: an independent nation (prior to December 1991, a part of the former Soviet Union), bounded on the west by Poland and the Baltic Sea.

mountains, one after the other, like caravans of camels with grey humps, and snow on top of them. And between the mountains there were valleys with green grass and bright red poppies. But that was not the main thing. Dad had brought back a kind of cap—black, with four corners and embroidered in white silk. It was called a tubeteika—you pronounced it "tyubbytaker." Dad showed it around and then put it in a cupboard, alongside a sombrero[10]—a broad straw hat from Argentina, and a svanka[11]—a white felt cap from the Caucasus.[12] "The start of our family collection of national head-dresses," said Dad.

Yesterday, Sunday, Andrius had taken the cap without permission. He wanted to show it off—although actually it was too big for him and kept slipping down over his nose instead of sitting smartly on the back of his head. Well, to make a long story short, he set off in the tubeteika to the bank of the Vilnia.[13] And bent over the water— and the tubeteika slid forward and—

"I ran along the bank and tried to keep up with it. I simply tore along but by the bridge—you know?—the water swirls around, a real whirlpool—and it was gone. Sucked down."

"And they don't know yet at home," said Dotas, half statement, half question.

"Would I be picking your brains if they knew?" sobbed Andrius, then, remembering, felt in his pocket and pulled out a stamp with a zebra and a chocolate in silver paper. The stamp was crumpled and the sweet had been flattened from long existence in his pocket. He held out his gifts to Dotas.

Dotas examined the stamp and then returned it.

"Defective—a reject."

"I didn't know," mumbled a confused Andrius. "I'll get you another. A whole series, with spiders!"

10. **sombrero** [som brer′ ō]
11. **svanka** [sfän′ kä]
12. **Caucasus** [kô′ kə səs]: a mountain range in Georgia, an independent nation (prior to December 1991, a part of the former Soviet Union).
13. **Vilnia** [vil′ nē ə]: a river in Lithuania.

Dotas nodded staidly[14] and relapsed into concentrated thought, chewing the chocolate. Promising folds appeared on his forehead.

"Listen, then. Ask your father what is the capital of Kirghizia. Secondly, how many schools there are. Only do it so that he doesn't suspect anything. That's all," he said at last.

"That's all?" repeated Andrius, disappointed.

"For the present—all. The rest comes later," said Dotas with a sly look. "Find out, and tell me." He turned on his heel and ran off home.

Just before going to bed that evening Andrius tackled his father, approaching in roundabout ways.

"Dad, what's the capital of Portugal?"

"Lisbon."

"Lisbon? And Estonia?"[15]

"You ought to know that! Tallinn."[16]

"Oh, of course—I'd forgotten. And Kirghizia?"

"Kirghizia? Frunze."[17]

"Frunze, Frunze, Frunze," he whispered to fix it in his mind. "And Dad! How many schools would there be in Frunze?"

"A good many, for certain."

"As many as thirty?"

"I expect so. They have a lot of children there."

"Thirty schools. And the forms[18]—I suppose they have them like ours—three A, three B, and so on all through the school."

"Of course. A and B and maybe C, D and E. I told you there are a lot of children."

"Smashing!"

"I'm glad to see you taking an interest in distant parts," said Dad approvingly. "You can always ask me if there's anything you want to know, I'll be glad to tell you."

---

14. **staidly** [stād′ lē]: thoughtfully, seriously.
15. **Estonia** [e′ stō nē ə]: an independent nation (prior to December 1991, a part of the former Soviet Union), bounded on the north by Finland.
16. **Tallinn** [tal′ ən]
17. **Frunze** [frün zə]: now called Bishkek.
18. **forms:** grade levels.

"Not less than thirty," Dotas repeated thoughtfully after he had heard Andrius's report during the first break. He did not hurry with his advice, and indeed, it seemed doubtful whether he had any to give because he suddenly asked, "What's your number in the form book?"

"Fifteen."

"Fifteen—that's better, in fact it's good," he mumbled. "Now, this is what you must do. Write to Frunze. To a pupil who is number fifteen in form 3B."

"But what shall I write?"

"Send some kind of souvenir—a postcard or a badge or something, and ask for a tubeteika."

"So that's it!"

So clever and yet so simple! Couldn't be simpler. Why couldn't he have thought of that himself? Obviously he felt disgusted with himself.

Dotas looked at him, narrow-eyed, and he suddenly wondered uneasily whether the wiseacre could read his thoughts and perhaps take offense.

"What a grand idea!" he flattered his counselor.

"Don't write only one letter," said the latter weightily. "Nothing might come of it. Write to all the thirty schools, address the letters school number one, two and so on, Frunze, Kirghizia. Pupil number fifteen in form three B—the three A and C too, all the threes."

"How many letters will that be? Surely I don't need so many."

"Better be safe. Let's see—four forms each in thirty schools—h'm! A hundred and twenty. Well, that makes it a sure thing, one of the hundred and twenty will certainly send it."

"Well—thanks awfully!"

"That's all right. If they send two, then one for me?"

"Of course!"

Woman's tubeteika, courtesy of Margaret Coleman, Director, Russian American Cultural Center, Russia Wharf, Boston

Then the work began. Andrius cut the pages of ten notebooks into neat sheets, emptied his collection of badges and pulled all the unused stamps out of his album. A hundred and twenty letters—that was no joke, he had not written so many in his whole life.

Dear unknown friend,

I do not yet know your name, but like me you are number fifteen in the form book and for that reason I am writing to you. I have had a piece of very bad luck. My dad was in Kirghizia and brought back a souvenir. A black tubeteika with white embroidery. And I accidentally dropped it in the river. Dad does not know yet but when he does there'll be bad trouble. Please save me, send me a tubeteika, and then let's go on corresponding. I am enclosing a souvenir, a badge from my city Vilnius. Write to me at school so that they do not know at home. That's all. All the best,

Andrius

"That's all right," said Dotas when Andrius showed him the letter and then asked him to add, "Dotas, a representative of Lithuanian youth, sends you greetings and would be very glad to make your acquaintance."

Andrius sighed but wrote it. A hundred and twenty times.

A week passed and then a second. Dad went away on another trip without discovering the loss of the tubeteika. Andrius lived in a torment of suspense until at last, one day in May, the teacher suddenly said, "Andrius, there's a parcel for you in the teacher's room, go and fetch it."

Andrius went with beating heart. A package wrapped in pink paper lay on the long table. Andrius picked it up, went out into the passage, then with trembling hands tore off the paper and pulled

out—a tubeteika!—exactly like the one Dad had brought, black, four-cornered and embroidered with white silk. Marvelous! And there was a letter, too.

Dear Andrius,

I was very pleased to get your letter. Thank you for the badge. I bought a tubeteika at once and am glad to give it to you. I have wanted for a long time to have a pen-friend in another republic. My mother says that there are no mountains in Lithuania and that you do not drink koumiss,[19] that is mare's milk. A pity because koumiss is very good, I love it. I collect butterflies, I have a lot. If you can, please catch a Lithuanian butterfly for me. Write me more about yourself and your friends and your school and your republic. And I will write, too. Greetings to your youth representative Dotas,

All the best,

Asan

Returning to the classroom, Andrius met Dotas's eyes. He wore a proudly triumphant look. They exchanged winks.

The next day again the teacher announced a parcel for Andrius.

Again Andrius stood before the long table—but this time he saw four packages. He did not even wait to open them—the contents were obvious; he scooped them up and scuttled back to the class-room. One tubeteika he would give the wiseacre as agreed, one for himself, but the third and fourth and fifth—? Oh, something would turn up.

After school Dotas tried on the tubeteika in the cloakroom.

"A bit big, but it'll do."

You might at least have said thank you, thought Andrius.

When the teacher summoned Andrius the next day she sounded puzzled.

Andrius went reluctantly, very unhappy, his legs like rubber. And with reason. The whole table was piled with almost identical

19. **koumiss** [kü′mis]

packages. A mountain of them! Fifty at least, maybe more. How on earth would he carry them all? And what was he to do with them? In his confusion it took him a long time to gather them up. And it was all the fault of that clever donkey Dotas.

Andrius carried the packages to the cloakroom, rolled them in his raincoat and tied the sleeves. When he returned to the classroom he did not even look at Dotas; but after school he grabbed the bundle and ran to overtake him, to give them all to him and let him do what he liked with them since he was so clever. However, Dotas heard panting behind him, turned, saw Andrius crimson with fury, and ran for his life.

"Stop!" howled Andrius. "Stop! These are yours! You hear me? Yours! You told me to write all those letters! Take them or I'll tell the teacher!"

But Dotas pelted off without turning.

When he got home Andrius dived into the cellar, found a clean sack, tipped all the packages into it, pushed it into a corner and covered it with all sorts of old rubbish. Later, he could get it out, read the letters and seek advice from his own wits, how on earth to get out of this new snarl he was in.

At school he kept very quiet. He did not want to be noticed. He never looked at Dotas.

At break the headmaster himself sought him out.

"I think you'd better explain the meaning of all this. Otherwise I'll have to send for your parents."

The pile of packages on the table in the teachers' room was as big as ever. Andrius looked at it, horrified.

"I—I'll explain—later," he whispered and rather surprisingly the headmaster left it at that.

It certainly was a case of out of the frying-pan. Andrius again collected the armful of packages, took them to the cloakroom and bundled them into his coat. Dotas had prudently[20] disappeared without waiting for the last lesson.

The sack in the cellar was almost full and nearly too heavy to lift.

20. **prudently** [prüd′ nt lē]: planned carefully ahead of time.

Later on he discovered a package he had pushed into his pocket and forgotten. He unwrapped it and saw a tubeteika—*such a tubeteika*, velvet, and embroidered with blue silk, and it fitted him perfectly, too. And a letter.

Dear distant Andrius,

What an unusual name but a nice one. The whole form envied me being the fifteenth and getting a letter from Lithuania. I was dreadfully upset about your needing a tubeteika so badly because I have not any money to buy one and send it at once. And I cannot ask mum. Dad was killed in a motor accident and I have nine brothers and sisters, three older than I am and the rest younger, so it is difficult for mum with all of us. But I asked auntie for velvet and silk and my sisters and friends have helped me. They all send you greetings. Do you like our tubeteika? I am so glad to give it to you, Andrius. My grandad and grandma live on the bank of a great big lake called Issyk-Kul.[21] It is beautiful there. Come and see it when you grow up. I must stop now but I shall be waiting for your reply. I would like to have you for a pen-friend.

Wishing you all the very best,

Aigyul[22]

Reading the letter Andrius felt himself blush for shame. He remembered it in the night and cried. He cried for a long time, and in the morning his whole face was swollen.

That day there were only three packages on the table. The flood was dwindling. The day after there was only a letter.

21. **Issyk-Kul** [is ik′ kəl]: a lake in northeastern Kirghizia.
22. **Aigyul** [a ig′ yül]

"Dear Andrius," wrote a boy called Tologen,[23] "I am sorry I cannot send you a tubeteika, I feel very bad about it but it is not my fault. I have been to all the shops where they have always had tubeteikas but now there was not one, they told me they had had plenty but they were all sold out. Actually, it is girls who wear tubeteikas here, boys wear a kind of felt hat with two little peaks. It is called ak-kalpak and it is boat-shaped. But please do not worry, as soon as any appear I will send you a tubeteika. I would like to have you for a pen-friend. I am enclosing a picture postcard of the Ala-Tau Mountains.[24] And please do send me pictures of Lithuania, especially the sea. I have never seen the sea but on the map Lithuania is right by it. Honestly, I tried to get you the tubeteika."

Andrius read this letter in the classroom during break and he had hardly finished when the monitor came and said the headmaster wanted him and added that the form mistress was already in his office.

To say Andrius was uncomfortable would be putting it mildly. He stared at his boots and his ears burned. And then—suddenly—he decided to make a clean breast of it all.

"But why did you send a hundred and twenty letters?" asked the headmaster. "Wouldn't one have been enough?"

"It was Dotas who advised me to." Andrius was no tell-tale, but since Dotas was avoiding him, then let people know the sort of adviser he was. "I wanted to write one but he said it must be a hundred and twenty. It took me three days, my hands were sore, and then he made me add a greeting from him."

23. **Tologen** [tō lō´ gən]
24. **Ala-Tau Mountains** [al ə´ taủ]: a part of a mountain range that extends from Kirghizia to the northeast of Issyk-Kul.

Now Dotas will get it, thought Andrius vengefully. Serve him right!

But the teacher only laughed. "You don't have to follow every bit of advice that's given. Use your own head! You're a head taller than he is and you get better marks, too!"

His eyes went down to his boots again. He was crimson with shame. It was true, he ought to have done his own thinking. He wasn't a bit of a kid. He would soon be in the fourth form.

At the end of the last lesson the teacher gave Dotas a meaning look.

"Well, wise adviser, what has your wisdom to offer now? You know what I'm talking about?"

"I know," said Dotas without any great sign of confusion.

"And what's your advice now?"

Dotas stared out of the window. It gave a view of the railway and a train with small green coaches, looking like toys in the distance. A fold appeared on the forehead of the sage.

Everybody knew the whole story by this time and all eyes were fixed on Dotas. How would he wriggle out of this one?

"My advice is," said Dotas with dignity, "to distribute the tubeteikas and letters to all those who'd like to have pen-friends in Kirghizia. There!"

"Good for you!" said the teacher.

Ak-kalpak, courtesy of Margaret Coleman, Director, Russian American Cultural Center, Russia Wharf, Boston

The form literally howled with delight and Andrius felt as though he had been sandbagged. Idiot—such a simple solution! Couldn't be simpler! Hand around the tubeteikas and let the kids answer the letters and have pen-friends and exchange souvenirs. Why hadn't he thought of it himself? Of course, he might have, but Dotas had thought of it first. It wasn't for nothing the kids said he'd a head on him!

It wasn't worth bearing a grudge against Dotas. There was too much to be done. He dragged the sack into the classroom and it wasn't only his pals from 3B who wanted to correspond with children in Kirghizia. A and C too were clamoring[25] for letters. Andrius kept Asan and Aigyul for himself, however. They would be his own friends.

Now the whole form dreams of visiting the Ala-Tau Mountains and Lake Issyk-Kul. They probably will, too, if not this summer, then the next. Dotas advises it, too.

25. **clamoring** [klam′ ər ing]: demanding noisily.

VYTAUTE ZILINSKAITE

Vytaute Zilinskaite was born in 1930 in Kaunas, Lithuania. She has seen—and is seeing—many changes in her country, which was part of the Union of Soviet Socialist Republics when she was growing up. Zilinskaite graduated from Vilnius University in 1955 and first began to publish in 1958. She has written poetry collections, a short novel, and short stories. Zilinskaite has won the State Prize of Lithuania twice. She now lives in Vilnius, the capital of her country. Her other books for young people include *The Robot and the Butterfly* and *Mike the Giant.*

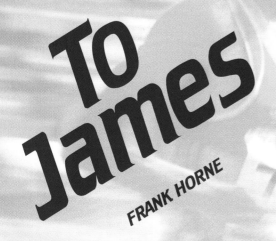

To James

FRANK HORNE

Do you remember
how you won
that last race . . . ?
how you flung your body
at the start . . .   5
how your spikes[1]
ripped the cinders[2]
in the stretch . . .
how you catapulted[3]
through the tape . . .   10
do you remember . . . ?
Don't you think
I lurched with you
out of those starting holes . . . ?
Don't you think   15
my sinews[4] tightened
at those first
few strides . . .
and when you flew into the stretch
was not all my thrill   20
of a thousand races
in your blood . . . ?
At your final drive
through the finish line
did not my shout   25
tell of the
triumphant ecstasy
of victory . . . ?

Live
as I have taught you 30
to run, Boy
it's a short dash.
Dig your starting holes
deep and firm
lurch out of them 35
into the straightaway[5]
with all the power
that is in you
look straight ahead
to the finish line 40
think only of the goal
run straight
run high
run hard
save nothing 45
and finish
with an ecstatic burst
that carries you
hurtling
through the tape to victory . . . 50

FRANK HORNE

Frank Horne [1899-1974] was born in Brooklyn, New York. After graduating from City College, he studied optometry in Illinois. Horne began practice as an eye doctor, but after four years he became a teacher at an industrial school in Georgia. Horne worked in Washington, D. C., in the middle of the Great Depression, first with the National Youth Administration and then moving on to Housing and Intergroup Relations. Horne founded the National Committee Against Discrimination in Housing.

Horne's writing followed his work. Poetry was the main form he chose, but he also wrote articles on subjects ranging from sports to education to housing. His writing was closely woven into his life. Horne suffered a great deal from physical pain and illness, yet when he had trouble walking, he wrote of runners such as the boy James in this poem.

1. **spikes:** sharp parts of running shoes that allow for firm footing.
2. **cinders:** ashes, partly burned coal, or finely ground rock used as the surface of a running track.
3. **catapulted** [kat′ ə pult əd]: sprung.
4. **sinews** [sin′ yüz]: tendons.
5. **straightaway** [strāt′ ə wā′]: the straight part of a track, between the last turn and the finish line.

JACKIE ROBINSON

LUCILLE CLIFTON

ran against walls
without breaking.
in night games
was not foul[1]
but, brave as a hit
over whitestone fences,
entered the conquering dark.

1. **foul:** in baseball, out of bounds.

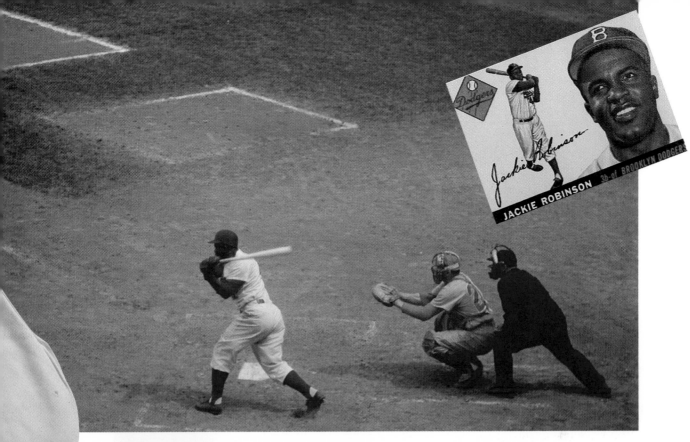

LUCILLE CLIFTON

Lucille Clifton was born in 1936 in Depew, New York. Her parents were laborers and had little formal education, but they raised their children on tales of Africa and strong women. Her mother read her own poems to young Lucille and her siblings.

It was a great blow to the family when Clifton dropped out of college, but she had resolved to become a writer. She wanted to be a poet like her mother; she wanted to be strong like her African forebears. It was a long time before her poems were published. Clifton married and raised six children first, but, as a result, her poems are for children as well as for adults. She writes of ordinary people who rise to challenges. Many of her poems echo African American speech and music. Clifton writes stories as well as poems, most of them for children. Her story *My Friend Jacob* tells of a winner different from Jackie Robinson.

A GIRL WHO WOULD BE COMMISH

from *The Atlanta Journal*

Sitkoff, 14, applies for baseball's top job

By Mike Fish
STAFF WRITER

It's a job any red-blooded American male would relish.[1] You get a comfortable New York office, along with seats to the game of your choice. And the pay isn't bad, either. The last guy made $650,000 a year.

Now, at least one female aspires[2] to be commissioner of baseball. And Erica Sitkoff is willing to run the game for free. The only catch is that she just turned 14. But that didn't stop the Marietta resident from sending a letter to the commissioner's office proposing herself as the replacement for the ousted Fay Vincent.[3]

"I wrote really just because there wasn't a commissioner," said Sitkoff, who will be a freshman at Wheeler High in the fall and describes herself as a loyal Atlanta Braves fan and a regular in the Terrell Mill Softball League. "It wasn't anything serious. It just seemed like they need someone."

In her letter to Bud Selig, Milwaukee Brewers owner and de facto[4] commissioner

Erica Sitkoff

of baseball in his position as chairman of the owner's Executive Council, Sitkoff said her every decision would be made in the "best interest of baseball."

1. **relish** [rel′ ish]: enjoy.
2. **aspires** [ə spīrz′]: seeks.
3. **Fay Vincent:** the former commisioner of baseball, who was fired.
4. **de facto** [di fak′ tō]: actual, although not officially chosen.

Selig forwarded the one-page inquiry to search committee chairman Bill Bartholomay, chairman of the board of the Braves. He responded in a letter, suggesting she "needed an education for the job, and to go to school first." (Sitkoff promised to continue her education by correspondence courses if she gets the job.)

"I thought it was wonderful," Bartholomay said. "But she's got some other things to do first, like get through high school and college. She sounds like a great candidate for 2006."

Sitkoff recently returned from a two-week visit in London with her father, Harvard Sitkoff, a history professor at the University of New Hampshire who was a visiting professor this summer at Cambridge.[5]

Sitkoff is among at least 180 applicants for the commissioner's job—including former U.S. Sen Wyche Fowler,[6] one-time Florida State president Bernie Sliger[7] and former U.S. Olympic Committee president Bill Hybl.[8] She is not, however, among the 30 candidates who have been granted interviews.

Bartholomay said the list has been whittled to fewer than 20, though noting that the search committee also would start considering baseball people this month. He said he is hopeful that a recommendation can be made to the Executive Council at a September meeting in Boston.

Office of the Commissioner,

I would like to apply for the position of commissioner of baseball. I have a genuine love, interest and knowledge of the game. I'd love the job.

Since I am just starting out, I'd like to work for free.

I avidly read about baseball and understand the game well. Every decision I make would be "in the best interest of baseball."

I think the owners would get along with me better than with past commissioners. Among my best qualities are those of leadership and organization.

If I were chosen for this position, I would continue my (ninth grade) education by correspondence courses.

Thank you for your time,

Erica Sitkoff

---

5. **Cambridge** [kām′ brij]: a university in England.
6. **Wyche Fowler** [wish foul′ ər]
7. **Bernie Sliger** [slī′ ger]
8. **Bill Hybl** [hī′ bl]

JAMES ALE

PHILLIP HOOSE

When he was nine, James Ale saw his friend get hit by a car when they were playing ball in a crowded street. It made him wonder, why should they have to play in the street when kids in the rich part of town had parks? The more he thought, the madder he got. Finally, James Ale took on town hall.

James Ale cried out as his friend Bobby Adams settled into position to catch the ball. Bobby was concentrating so hard that he didn't hear the white Thunderbird[1] as it tore around the corner, heading toward him. He was on the ground, his leg bent in pain, before he even knew what happened.

James and his friends live in Davie, Florida, on the edge of the Everglades.[2] Davie is really two towns. The western part is where rich people from Miami build ranches and keep their horses. The eastern part, where James and Bobby live, is a neighborhood of small trailers and condominiums[3] on tiny lots.

1. **Thunderbird:** a type of automobile made by Ford Motor Company.
2. **Everglades:** a swampy region in southern Florida.
3. **condominiums** [kon də min′ ē əms]: groups of units or homes that are individually owned, with the land owned in common by all property owners in the group.

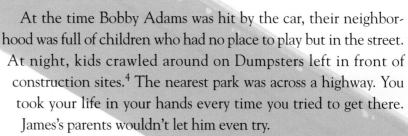

At the time Bobby Adams was hit by the car, their neighborhood was full of children who had no place to play but in the street. At night, kids crawled around on Dumpsters left in front of construction sites.[4] The nearest park was across a highway. You took your life in your hands every time you tried to get there. James's parents wouldn't let him even try.

As the sound of Bobby's ambulance faded into the distance, James walked slowly home. He was angry. Bobby wouldn't have gotten hurt if they had a park to play in. But officials never spent any money in this part of town.

James looked over at a small worn field right behind the water plant. That would be a perfect place for a park. There could be a playground at one end for the little kids and a basketball court at the other end. And some lights. Everyone would use it.

In that moment, James decided to make it happen. He'd organize the kids, and they'd beat down the mayor's door. They'd call themselves Children for Davie. So what if he was only nine?

That evening, James asked his dad for advice. As president of the local condominium association, John Ale was always going off to the town council[5] meetings. If anyone would know how to pressure Davie's government, his dad would.

John Ale listened carefully to his son's idea before speaking. "You'll have to know exactly what you want and be able to prove that it's important. Playground equipment will cost money, and people ask the mayor and the town council for money every day," he said. "Everyone thinks their project is the most important thing in the world, and there's only so much tax money to go around."

4. **construction sites** [kən struk′ shən sīts′]: places where something is being built.
5. **town council** [koun′ səl]: a group of persons elected by citizens to make laws for and manage a town.

Father and son sat together in silence. "But you can do it," Mr. Ale said. "More than anything, you'll have to be persistent.[6] You can't quit."

Preparing for Action

James decided to start at the top. The next day, he telephoned the mayor.

"Mayor Kovac's office," said a pleasant voice.

"May I talk to the mayor?"

"She's not in. May I take a message?"

James left his name and telephone number. A few hours later, the mayor called him back. "I told her what had happened to Bobby Adams and said we needed a park in our neighborhood," James recalls. "I could tell she wasn't paying much attention. She seemed to be in a hurry. All she said was that she'd look into it and call me back."

"A while later she did. She said once there had been a park in our area and it had been vandalized.[7] It was like we had blown our only chance. Then she didn't say anything. Finally, I just said, 'Well, I think we need a park,' and we hung up. I felt discouraged. She treated me like a kid. I had to get her to pay attention."

James went to his room, flicked on his computer, and typed *Children for Davie* in bold print at the top of the screen. Below that, he typed out a petition[8] calling for a new park. "Please sign this if you think that it would be better for our neighborhood if there were a park," it concluded.[9] Beneath that he put blanks for signatures.

He printed it out, snapped it onto a clipboard, and went outside to try to get kids to sign it. They squinted[10] at his petition, then looked at him as if he were crazy.

6. **persistent** [pər sis′ tənt]: not giving up, especially in the face of dislike, disapproval, or difficulties.
7. **vandalized** [van′ dl īzd]: destroyed senselessly, without reason or cause.
8. **petition** [pə tish′ ən]: a written application for action by a judge or some authority.
9. **concluded** [kən klüd′ əd]: ended.
10. **squinted** [skwint′ əd]: looked at with suspicion, with eyes partly closed.

"Sure, man, *you're* gonna get us a park."

"Well, don't you think we need one? Look what happened to Bobby."

"Yeah, we need one, but who's gonna listen to *you?*"

"Not just me. We'll all go. She'll have to listen to all of us."

"You're outa your mind." They were starting to drift away.

"Well, just sign it if you're for it, okay?"

James got fifty kids to sign, but no one would go with him to see the mayor, not even Bobby Adams, who by now was back from the hospital and recovering from a broken leg.

James called the mayor again, this time asking for an appointment to talk about the park in person. She said yes. James prepared carefully for that meeting. Above all, he needed to be taken seriously. Here's what he did:

❑ He gathered more signatures on his petition.

❑ He took a map of Davie and outlined the site where he wanted the park, so the mayor would know just where it should be.

❑ He typed out a letter on his Children for Davie stationery to leave with the mayor, listing the reasons why the park should be built and stating exactly what the town should provide: swings, a slide, monkey bars, a basketball court, and lights.

❑ He made up some business cards on his computer. They said, "James Ale, President, Children for Davie."

On the afternoon of the meeting, James put on his red suit jacket, a red shirt, and gray pants and squeezed into his hard black shoes. He combed his hair carefully. "When the time came for my mom to pick me up and drive me over there, I was ready."

"It Should Be Here."

Mayor Joan Kovac had expected James Ale to be a child who maybe wanted to tell his friends he had met the mayor in person. But the boy who walked through the door had business on his mind. "He came in with a briefcase," she recalls. "And then he handed me a business card."

Looking directly at her, James told the mayor that his neighborhood was unsafe for kids. They had no place to play. They needed a park. It would help the town, he said, because it would save lives. The crime rate would go down because kids would have something to do. Mayor Kovac was leaning forward, looking right at him and listening carefully. When he finished, she got up and walked around her desk to a map of Davie. She pointed to three dots, clustered together on the west side of town.

"We're building three new parks right now, James," she said. "Can't your parents take you to one of them?"

"No," said James. "My parents both work. So do everyone else's around me. Those parks are a long way from us. We need a place of our own."

The mayor looked at the map again. "But there's no empty land where you live. Everything's all built up. Do you have a suggestion?"

James pulled the map from his briefcase and spread it on the mayor's desk. "It should be here," he said, pointing to the square he had drawn. "Behind the water plant. It's the right place. Look at this petition from the kids in the neighborhood. Everyone agrees."

Mayor Kovac had no choice but to respect him. He wasn't criticizing her or blaming the town. He had come to her with a plan. He was representing a group, and he wanted her support. She had to consider his proposal.[11]

"Well," she said at last, "let me talk to some people in the Parks Department. We'll have to visit the site. I can't make any promises now, but I can promise I won't just put you off."

James got up and extended his hand, smiling. He pointed to his card on her desk. "My phone number is right here," he said. "I look forward to hearing from you."

"We're Going to Build That Kid a Park."

One Saturday morning a few weeks later, James met the mayor and the town administrator[12] behind the water tower. James had been studying up on how Davie's government worked. The mayor and the town administrator were Davie's two most important officials. Along with the town attorney and the five members of the town council, they made the big decisions on how to run Davie's business. The town administrator did most of the detailed, day-to-day business.

James had gone to meet with him, too. He was a nice enough man—he had even given James tickets to a wrestling meet—but he

11. **proposal** [prə pō′ zəl]: a plan, suggestion, or scheme.
12. **town administrator** [ad min′ ə strā′ tər]: the person who manages the day-to-day, detailed business of a town, usually an appointed position.

didn't seem very interested in the park. Still, he had agreed to visit the site. Now James had the town's two most important people together right where he wanted them. This was his chance.

First James pointed to the spot where Bobby Adams had been hit. Several kids were running around. They had to agree that it would be hard for a turning car to see them.

Then James walked them around the small field. "This is the perfect place for us," James said. The administrator frowned. The lot was too small for a park, he said. He advised James to be patient. Someday the town would tear down a couple of houses and build the kids a real park.

"We don't want to wait for a bigger park" James said flatly. "We need this park, here and now. This is the right place. It will get used. You already own the land, and we're just talking about playground equipment. We're not asking for much." He could see the man's mind was closed.

If they thought James Ale would go away, they were wrong. He waited for a few days for an answer, and when none came, he tried even harder. Nearly every day after school, he wrote brief, carefully worded letters to town officials. He also sent them updated copies of his ever-growing petition.

One night he called the secretary assigned to the town council and asked if, representing Children for Davie, he could speak briefly to the council members at Wednesday night's meeting.

"Are you a voter?" the secretary asked.

"Well, no, but I—"

"Then the answer is no," she said firmly.

James turned up the heat. He called the reporter for a Miami newspaper assigned to Davie and offered him the story of a young boy taking on town hall for the kids in his neighborhood. The reporter accepted, and a story soon appeared in the newspaper. James sent a copy to town officials.

Every few days, he called Mayor Kovac and asked her for a progress report. He was always polite. Did she need any more information? Was there anything he could do to help?

Finally his work paid off. One evening after school, James was surprised to receive a call from the town council's secretary inviting him to a council meeting. The next Wednesday evening, Mayor Kovac announced the creation of a new park. Asking him to stand, she introduced James by saying, "This boy could teach a lot of adults I know a few things about lobbying[13] town government."

Mayor Kovac says that the small area that everyone in Davie now calls James Ale Park has become the most popular playground site in Davie. "I drive by it, and there are never fewer than thirty kids there," she says. "The parks we built in the richer parts of town are barely used. James was right."

The kids in the neighborhood thought it was a miracle that a nine-year-old boy actually got his town to spend five thousand

13. **lobbying:** trying to influence the members of a lawmaking body.

dollars to build a park for them. But it wasn't a miracle. He simply used tried-and-true lobbying techniques.

In Mayor Kovac's words:
❏ James went right to the person who had power—me, in this case—and got to know me. It was smart, because lobbying is partly personal. I like James. ❏ He came with a very specific plan. He had it in writing so that I could show it to people. ❏ His petition showed that he was representing other children. ❏ He was able to say, in a very few words, why that park was needed. And I could tell he really believed in it. ❏ He didn't come with a budget—probably he should have—but he knew what he wanted at the park. That made it easy for me to figure out the cost. ❏ He was always available to meet officials at the site. He provided information that we needed. He was on time. ❏ He was respectful. He kept pressure on us without being obnoxious[14] or turning us off. And he listened to me. ❏ He was persistent. That's the most important thing of all. He just never gave up. I don't think he ever would have. ❏ One other thing. He paid me back, and in the right way. When my campaign for reelection came up, James called and asked if he could help. He went door-to-door asking people to vote for me. I mean he really *blitzed* that neighborhood. He was an asset to me. During the campaign, I listed the creation of James Ale Park as one of my major accomplishments.

14. **obnoxious** [əb nok′ shəs]: very disagreeable; offensive, rude, bad-mannered.

And what did James learn? "I learned a lot. People in government will tell a kid that they don't have time for little things like a park," James says. "But if you think about it, it really is a big thing. I had a good idea and I never gave up. Kids have rights, too. But we have to learn to use them."

PHILLIP HOOSE

Phillip Hoose was born in 1942 in South Bend, Indiana. He has long been interested in ecology and has a master's degree in environmental science. He recalls that as a child he often saw "things that I thought were wrong, but there was no one to help me." It seemed that "only adults mattered," when it came to changing things. However, when he was grown, Hoose watched his own very young children succeed in raising a large sum of money for the homeless. Kids *could* change things.

Hoose went on a search for other young people who had been able to take action in their communities. He found them. He interviewed many young people in several countries and chose James Ale's story among others for his book *It's Our World, Too!*

Hoose says he has found that adults listen when a young person knows how to approach a problem. They are impressed if it is a young person who is informed and business-like and refuses to be discouraged.

"I wish I'd had a book like this," Hoose says. He thinks he would have felt stronger when he was young, had he known other people his age who were trying to make their world a better place.

Hoose is a staff member of the Nature Conservancy, working to preserve the habitats of endangered species.

Asking Big Questions About the Literature

Why are goals important?

Write a Testimonial
SPEECH

Imagine that you've been invited to a banquet to honor the efforts and accomplishments of the characters in this unit. Write a speech in which you congratulate three characters on their success. Begin your speech with an explanation of what you learned about the importance of goals from reading this unit.

MAKE A SUMMARY CHART

Make a chart of the characters in this unit, their goals, and why the goals were important. In the column headed *Goals*, list the goals the characters hoped to accomplish. Label the ones they did accomplish with an *A* for *achieved*. For those not yet accomplished, use *T* for *trying*. When you are finished, compare your chart with others in your class. Notice the different goals identified by your classmates.

LITERATURE STUDY
Character

Most stories have more than one character. The goals of the main **character,** or protagonist, give direction to the action in the story. Without this character the story could not go forward. With a partner, agree on a main character from this unit whose dedication to her or his goals helped you understand the importance of goals. Together write a paragraph explaining your decision. (*See* "Character" *on page 119.*)

Character/Title	Goals	Why Important
Lupe Medrano "The Marble Champ"	1. To win at a sport (A)	Made Lupe feel good about herself.

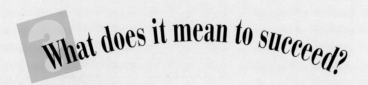

What does it mean to succeed?

Theme

The **theme** is the main idea or message that a piece of literature expresses. The theme of this unit is "Keep trying—for success comes to those with persistence."

Write a letter to the character in this unit whose success inspired you the most. Tell why the character's success inspired you. (*See "Theme" on page 118.*)

Success Stories in History

History is full of success stories—inventors, soldiers, and everyday people. Use a library reference book like *Chambers's Biographical Dictionary* or *Who's Who in America* to find out more about a person you admire for his or her success. Make an outline of the information you find. Use the outline shown here as a guide. Prepare a presentation to your class. Tell about the person, the goal, and the invention, creation, or accomplishment.

Create A GREAT ACHIEVER COLLAGE

Real people often achieve great things. Using pictures you draw or photos cut from newspapers or magazines, make a collage that shows some of these great achievers. Include headlines and captions too. Add your favorite achiever from the unit by drawing a picture or creating a headline that tells about the success of the character. Then share and discuss your collage with your classmates.

Use the Person's Name as the Title

I. Tell the Person's Background
  A. List at least 2 details about his or her life

  B.

  C.

II. Tell the Person's Goal
  A. List at least 2 facts about the goal

  B.

  C.

III. Tell the Accomplishment
  A. Provide at least 2 details

  B.

  C.

Asking Big Questions About the Literature

Practice Makes Perfect

To an outfielder, *practice makes perfect* means catching fly balls over and over before a game to avoid dropping one during a game. What do you think the expression *practice makes perfect* might mean to the characters in this unit? Choose one character and write a paragraph that tells how *practice makes perfect* applies to that character.

STEPS IN A PROCESS

With a partner, choose a selection from this unit in which the character took a number of steps before reaching the goal or achieving the desired result. Draw an event chain similar to the one shown here. Fill in each block with an event from the story that helped the character achieve the final outcome. Compare your event chain with those drawn by your classmates. Discuss what each chain shows about persistence.

Outcome:

LITERATURE STUDY

Theme

The message "If at first you don't succeed, try, try again" tells the **theme,** or main idea, of the selections in this unit. People who "try, try again" show they are strong, determined, dedicated individuals. They don't always succeed, but they keep on trying. Write a poem about a time you had to "try, try again." You may choose to make your poem rhyme or to use free verse. (*See "Theme" on page 118.*)

How can people support others?

Character

You learned many details about the qualities of the main **characters,** or protagonists, as you read this unit. Some were dedicated and hard-working. Others were creative and self-assured.

Working with a partner or group, imagine that you must advertise for a new member to add to your team. You'll want someone who'll support the team. You'll probably want someone with the qualities you read about in this unit. Complete a character map so that you'll know the kind of person to ask for in the advertisement. Write each desirable quality in a circle. (*See "Character" on page 119.*)

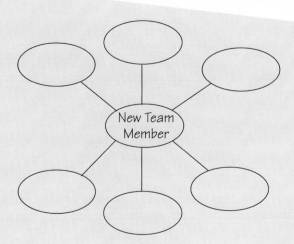

New Team Member

PLAY a Role

With a partner, role-play a situation in which you need help or support to solve a problem, complete a project, or learn a skill. How would you act if you were the person needing help? As the person offering support, what would you do? Try to give support in more than one way. The experiences of the characters in this unit might give you ideas.

Write a
LETTER OF SUPPORT

Perhaps someone in your school or community wants to start a recycling project, help homeless people, or get a playground built. Write a letter to the editor of your school or local newspaper explaining why you support that goal. Urge others to support the goal, too, and explain how each person might help.

NOW Choose a Project!

Three project choices involving goal setting, persistence, and support are described on the following pages.

Writing Workshop

Success is measured in many different ways. The Big Questions in this unit all deal with what it means to succeed and how to achieve success. Sometimes success means being able to help others. What skills do you have? What do you do well? The **purpose** of this project is to write a How-to Guide about your skill and then demonstrate that skill to your classmates—your **audience.**

Prewriting
GETTING STARTED

To begin, try brainstorming in your journal. For five to seven minutes, make a list of all the things you do well. Include things you do in school or at home—a sport, a hobby, or a chore you do for others.

Things I'm Good At

- make an origami fish
- play first base
- read aloud
- swim ~~crawl~~, freestyle
- ~~play~~ play trumpet ———
- wash windows
- carve a pumpkin

Prewriting
CHOOSING A TOPIC

When your list is complete, choose a topic that you can explain in clear, simple steps. Sinking a lay-up shot is a good topic because you can break it into steps—telling what to do first, second, third, and so on. It might not be as easy to explain how to swim. Instead, you might explain just one stroke such as the backstroke or freestyle.

Choose a topic that you can demonstrate to the class or a small group. Can you demonstrate how to sink a lay-up shot in the classroom without a real basketball and hoop? Could you make some props like a tiny net with a backboard and a small ball? Or would it be easier to show how to fold an origami bird or how to weave a simple cotton bracelet?

Prewriting
ORGANIZING IDEAS

Once you have a skill in mind, write down every idea you can think of that explains how to do it. Include where you do it, how it works best, and the materials you use. Think about the separate actions that make up the process and how long each one takes. Concentrate on discovering everything that leads to your success.

Organize your ideas by numbering them. Decide which you do first, second, third, and so on. Continue this process until you've decided on the order for all your details.

Freestyle
1. not as easy as it looks
1. useful if you like the water
3 windmill arm stroke
5. tilt head – breathing
3. slice through water
6. cup hands arch feet
4. kicking alone then moving arms
4 floating with arms in V
2. practice in shallow water
5. gulp air – blow bubbles through nose

Drafting YOUR HOW-TO GUIDE

Using your numbered list of details and keeping your audience in mind, you're ready to draft your How-to Guide. A good opening introduces the subject and creates interest. Your How-to Guide needs a topic sentence and an opening paragraph. In the opening paragraph of "How-to Guide: Freestyle Swimming" on pages 110-111, Gina Maggio, a student writer, mentions that her skill can help save your life.

Tips for Writing an Opening Paragraph

- Tell why the process is useful, important, or worth knowing.
- Make the process itself seem easy, fun, or necessary.
- Explain the advantages of knowing how to do this particular thing.
- Start out with an interesting or fun fact about the process.

After the opening paragraph, tell what materials are needed. Be specific. For example, "a 12" x 2" strip of cardboard" is clearer than "some cardboard." Gina tells you to practice where "your head is above the water when your hands touch the bottom."

Use each group of numbered details to create a paragraph about one step in the process. Add details as you think of them. But don't worry about including every detail in your first draft.

As you write your draft, keep in mind that your **purpose** is to write a How-to Guide for an **audience** of your classmates, so that they can be as successful at a skill as you are. To help keep your steps in order, include some of these words and phrases: *first, second, third, last, then, during, while, until, after,* and *at the same time.* Because Gina included many of these transition words and phrases in her How-to Guide, the steps are easy to follow.

Revising
YOUR GUIDE

Is the process you've explained clear and easy to understand? Ask a classmate to read your guide and do the steps as you've described them. Are the steps easy to follow? Check to see that you've put only one step of the process in each paragraph. Also be sure you fully explain one step before going on to the next. Look at the model on pages 110-111—"How-to Guide: Freestyle Swimming."

Editing
YOUR GUIDE

A missing period or comma can make two steps sound like one and could mean the difference between success and failure. After you've revised your draft, work with a partner to edit your guide. Read it to find any errors in spelling, grammar, and punctuation. Correct your errors and make a publishable copy of your How-to Guide.

Publishing
GIVING A TALK

When you've finished revising and editing, use your paper to help present the process to your classmates. Make up note cards. Gather any props you need. Then practice presenting the process.

Tips for Giving a Demonstration

- Speak slowly and clearly.
- Present the process in order. Don't forget transition words such as *first* and *next*.
- If you use props, check that everything works before you start. During the talk, be sure that everyone can see what you're doing.
- Pause for a moment after each step. Make sure your listeners follow the process.
- Use your voice to create interest. Keep your audience involved.

How-to Guide: Freestyle Swimming

by Gina Maggio, Orland Park, Illinois

Freestyle swimming is a stroke that is not as easy as it looks. It can take time and effort to perfect, but it is a useful stroke to know if you like to do activities in or on the water. This stroke is also helpful if you should get into trouble in the water. Learning to swim well can help save your life.

When you start to learn, make sure that the water you are practicing in is shallow enough so your head is above the water when your hands touch the bottom.

In freestyle swimming, your arms move in a windmill manner. Begin with both arms at your sides. Then reach out with your right hand and then your left. Move one arm in a circle from the shoulder, then the other. Bring your hand back, then up and over, and finally down in front to where it started. You might want to practice this standing up in or out of the water. In the beginning, make your hands straight and stiff so they slice through the water.

After you have learned the motion with your arms, you can start kicking. First, float with both arms in front of you, forming a V with your hands touching. Next practice kicking your legs up and down. Practice with your face in the water.

When you feel ready, you can start moving your arms in the windmill motion while you are kicking. At first, you should practice with your face in the water while kicking and moving your arms in the windmill manner. As time progresses, you can use breathing techniques.

The first step to learning breathing techniques is to blow

bubbles through your nose in the water. Next add the windmill motion of your arms. When your right arm touches your hip, tilt your head slightly out of the water to your right or left, whichever side is comfortable. When tilting your head, take a gulp of air through your mouth. As your arms move, return your face to the water and blow out air through your nose. When your face reaches the water, your right arm and hand should be just touching the water. You're making the next stroke.

When you have completed the steps above and feel you are ready, you can start improving how you swim by moving your arms and legs differently. When you started with your arms, you sliced through the water. Now you can make yourself go faster by cupping the water. This means that when your hand touches or is under the water, you can cup your hand so you can paddle yourself faster. Only when your hand is out of the water should it be in a slice position. If you keep your hand cupped in the air, you slow yourself down by taking in more air as your hand is raised.

Another suggestion for improving your swimming is to adjust your kicking technique. You can kick better if you arch your feet. This also helps you move faster through the water because you make less of a splash.

As you can see, the freestyle stroke is not as easy as it looks. It takes time and effort to perfect. As mentioned, this stroke can be helpful and useful. You can now go swimming knowing one more great stroke.

Cooperative Learning

DAY ONE AT A NEW SCHOOL

What advice would you give a younger student about how to succeed in school? In this project, you'll work with a group to create a booklet of advice for younger students. You'll decide on topics that should be included, on the best ways to present the advice, and on how to divide the work. Keep working at it until you come up with a booklet that will help fifth graders become successful sixth graders.

The SOLUTION

Think back to the beginning of this school year. What challenges and problems did you face when you started sixth grade? What did you do to make sixth grade a successful experience? To make a helpful booklet, you'll need to come up with both the problems and the solutions. They can be treated in a serious or funny way. The problems will help you decide what to put on each page of the booklet. Use a chart like this one to help your group collect ideas.

Problem	Item	Purpose of the Item
School is so big kids get lost	Make a map	Real map (scale should be correct) Add cartoon ideas for some locations
Move from class to class <u>on time</u>	Advice column	Don't go to your locker between classes—be prepared Don't stop to talk to other students
Missing the bus	Schedules	Late bus, where it goes and when

The BOOKLET

Once you have ideas for your booklet, you still have decisions to make. Will art make your booklet look serious or funny? Will you make several copies or just one? Choose the size—pocket-size if each fifth grader gets one or display-size if each class gets one. How will you bind it or hold it together? What about the cover? Who will create each part of the booklet and put it together? Make a copy of a project planner in your journal and use it to record the group's decisions.

Task	Who	When
Writing pages		
Drawing art		
Collecting photos		
Polling students		
Checking with teachers		

The PRESENTATION

How will students learn about your booklet? You might give each fifth-grade classroom a display copy for the class to examine as time permits. Or, as a group, you could explain its use. If each student will be given a booklet, distribute them after the presentation. In addition, you might combine the presentation with a tour of the middle school. Whichever way you choose, you'll have helped other students become more successful as they enter sixth grade.

Helping Your Community

EVERYONE HAS SKILLS FOR SUCCESS

Everyone loves to succeed at something. Very young children especially enjoy games and contests in which everyone wins. In this project, you'll plan an Everybody Wins Olympics for children in kindergarten or first grade.

Planning THE GAMES

With a partner or team, think of children in your school system or community who would enjoy an Everybody Wins Olympics. A nearby kindergarten or first-grade class, a group of children at a local hospital, or those at a day-care center might welcome your efforts.

Next brainstorm a list of games that will be fun for every child in the group. Keep in mind that these games must be very simple—naming colors or singing songs and making music, building things with blocks and collecting shapes, or, for some children, sack races and dashes. In your journal, make a chart like the one shown here. Record your ideas for as many kinds of games, abilities, and interests as possible.

EVERYBODY WINS
OLYMPICS

GAMES . . .
. sack races
. find the shape

ABILITIES . . .
. singing
. hopping
. running

INTERESTS . . .
. board games
→ sports
. building things

Planning is especially important when working with very young children. Think about how you'll divide children into groups and ways to show them how to play the games. Use these guidelines for giving directions.

Tips for Giving Oral Directions

- Speak slowly. Look at the children.
- Stand in a relaxed position. Bend or squat to be at eye level for very young children.
- Explain who will play, what they will do, and where they will do it.
- Tell children when they will start and how they will know when they are done.
- Speak so that you can be heard, but don't shout.

Planning THE PRIZES

To make sure everyone feels like a winner, every child should get a prize. Give awards for more than first, second, and third place. Give prizes for effort and originality. Who actually wins a race might not matter at all!

As a group, decide on ribbons, medals, or other prizes. Draw or describe them in your journal. Make a plan for who will get materials, make the rewards, and decorate them.

The PRESENTATION

Once you've planned the Everybody Wins Olympics, tell members of the community about them. Advertise in a local newspaper or learn the guidelines for public announcements at a local radio station and write one. You'll win by helping others.

Putting It All Together

What Have You Learned About Persistence?

In *Try, Try Again*, you learned that persistence helps people reach goals, find satisfaction, and help others. Think about how your ideas about this theme have changed. Look back at the writing you've done for this unit—in your journal, in response to your reading, and in the Writing Workshop. Share your thoughts about your own personal best with your classmates. Write a poem, a personal essay, or an autobiographical sketch about a goal you set for yourself. Tell what you've done to reach that goal and how close you've come to success. Then, with your classmates, create a Personal Best display in your classroom.

PERSONAL BEST

Prewriting and Drafting   Brainstorm a list of ways you've improved this year. Include any area where you've made a serious effort—school work, a sport, a hobby, or any personal activity. Choose the area of improvement that means the most to you.

Begin the draft of your poem, personal essay, or autobiographical sketch by telling what you wanted to do better and why. Next, tell all the things you did to improve. Put the steps in order. Use words such as *first, second, next,* and *after that.* End with how you feel about your effort or what you still want to do. You might encourage others to reach for their own personal best.

Revising and Editing   Share your draft with a partner. Ask for ideas to make it clearer or more interesting. In turn, think of things you like about your partner's draft and let your partner know. Your draft should tell how hard you tried for a personal best, so keep working on it until you're sure it does. Check the grammar, punctuation, and spelling too.

Publishing   Set up a Personal Best display area in your classroom. Along with your written work, include any objects or pictures that help show the goal you worked toward and all the steps you took to achieve that goal.

Evaluating Your Work

Think Back About the Big Questions

With a partner, discuss the Big Questions on pages 10-11. Do you have trouble answering any of these questions now? In your journal, write two or three sentences discussing how your responses to the Big Questions have changed after your work in this unit.

Think Back About Your Work

Now think back about the unit you've just finished and evaluate your work, including your reading, your writing, your activities, and your projects. Be kind to yourself, but be honest too!

Write a "Personal Persistence Profile" for your teacher. In your profile, explain what you've done during this unit and what you've learned. Use the following questions to help you write your profile.

- Which literature selections in this unit helped you the most to understand the importance of persistence? Why?

- What was your favorite activity in this unit? Why?

- What was your least favorite activity? Why?

- If you were to do your project again, what parts would you do the same way? On what parts would you be more persistent?

- What did you learn as you worked on your project?

- What have you learned in this unit about persistence?

- How would you rate your work in this unit? Use the following scale and give at least three reasons for your rating.

1 = Outstanding	3 = Fair
2 = Good	4 = Not as good as it could have been

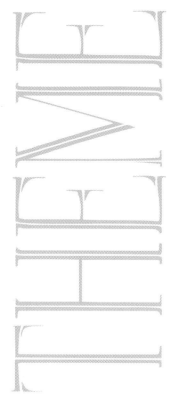

What Is Theme?

A **theme** is a general idea about people or life. It is the message an author communicates through the characters and the way they react to things that happen. A *universal theme* applies to people all over the world. The theme is not the same as the subject. It is not a summary of the plot. A subject can be expressed in one or two words (persistence). A theme must be expressed in a full sentence. (People who never give up often receive unexpected rewards.) Most often the theme is not stated directly. Instead, it is *implied*—the reader must look carefully at what the story suggests about life or the actions of human beings in order to discover the theme.

Identifying a Theme To preview a selection, you read the title and skim through the pages for photos or art that help you know what to expect. If a selection has a subtitle, you'll learn even more about it in a preview. A statement of the theme would make a good subtitle for a selection. Work with a partner to identify the themes in the selections in this unit. Together write subtitles for the selections. Finally see whether classmates can guess the selection by listening to the subtitle you created.

Changing the Theme The theme of a selection is suggested by the actions of the characters and the outcome of those actions. If the actions change, the outcome can be entirely different and the theme will change. Think of an experience you've had that you now wish you'd handled differently—where different actions would have created a different outcome. Write a description of that experience and how you would change it if you could. Then write a theme statement suggested by the real outcome and a theme statement you wish could be true.

What Is Character?

A **character** is a person or an animal that participates in the action of a work of literature. Through *characterization* writers create characters who seem real. They are active, changeable, and lifelike. To create such a character, a writer may use dialogue. In the character's own words or from what others say about the character, the reader learns enough to be able to guess what the character might do as the story progresses. The character's appearance and actions also help the reader know him or her as they might know a real person. Some characters, however, always remain the same. Such characters seem to have only one main quality. The writer provides few details about such flat characters.

Meeting Each Other   Each day you meet new and interesting characters through your reading. With a partner, select one character from each of two selections in this unit who might like to meet each other. Imagine a conversation between the two characters. What could they tell one another about persistence and how they succeeded? Role-play such a meeting or write the dialogue of their conversation. Make sure you have the characters introduce themselves. Remember, they have never met.

Adding Interest   Not all characters mentioned in the selections are main characters. Think about the characters who play very small parts in the stories. Choose one of these characters and make him or her more lifelike. Use a writer's methods of characterization to create a character who seems like a real person. For your character sketch, you may need more than one paragraph. Keep working until you have a fully developed, interesting character who easily could become a main character in another story.

GLOSSARY OF LITERARY TERMS

A

alliteration Repetition of the first sound—usually a consonant sound—in several words of a sentence or a line of poetry.

allusion An author's indirect reference to someone or something that is presumed to be familiar to the reader.

anecdote A short narrative about an interesting or humorous event, usually in the life of a person.

antagonist The person or force opposing the protagonist or main character in a literary work. [See also *protagonist*.]

autobiography A person's written account of his or her own life.

B

ballad A poem, often a song, that tells a story in simple verse.

biography An account of a person's life, written by another person.

blank verse Unrhymed poetry.

C

character A person or an animal that participates in the action of a work of literature. A *dynamic character* is one whose thoughts, feelings, and actions are changeable and lifelike; a *static character* always remains the same. [See also *protagonist, antagonist*.]

characterization The creation of characters through the characters' use of language and through descriptions of their appearance, thoughts, emotions, and actions. [See also *character*.]

chronology An arrangement of events in the order in which they happen.

cliché An overused expression that sounds trite rather than meaningful.

climax The highest point of tension in the plot of a work of literature. [See also *plot*.]

comedy An amusing play that has a happy ending.

conclusion The final part or ending of a piece of literature.

concrete poem A poem arranged on the page so that its punctuation, letters, and lines make the shape of the subject of the poem.

conflict A problem that confronts the characters in a piece of literature. The conflict may be *internal* (a character's struggle within himself or herself) or *external* (a character's struggle against nature, another person, or society). [See also *plot*.]

context The general sense of words that helps readers to understand the meaning of unfamiliar words and phrases in a piece of writing.

D

description An author's use of words to give the reader or listener a mental picture, impression, or understanding of a person, place, thing, event, or idea.

dialect A form of speech spoken by people in a particular group or geographical region that differs in vocabulary, grammar, and pronunciation from the standard language.

dialogue The spoken words and conversation of characters in a work of literature.

drama A play that is performed before an audience according to stage directions and using dialogue. Classical drama has two genres: *tragedy* and *comedy*. Modern drama includes *melodrama, satire, theater of the absurd*, and *pantomime*. [See also *comedy, play*, and *tragedy*.]

dramatic poetry A play written in the form of poetry.

E

epic A long narrative poem written in a formal style and meant to be read aloud that relates the adventures and experiences of one or more great heroes or heroines.

essay   Personal nonfiction writing about a particular subject that is important to the writer.

excerpt   A passage from a larger work that has been taken out of its context to be used for a special purpose.

exposition   Writing that explains, analyzes, or defines.

extended metaphor   An elaborately drawn out metaphor. [See also *metaphor*.]

F

fable   A short, simple story whose purpose is to teach a lesson, usually with animal characters who talk and act like people.

fantasy   Imaginative fiction about unrealistic characters, places, and events.

fiction   Literature, including the short story and the novel, that tells about imaginary people and events.

figurative language Language used to express ideas through figures of speech: descriptions that aren't meant to be taken literally. Types of figurative language include *simile, metaphor, extended metaphor, hyperbole,* and *personification*.

figure of speech   A type of figurative language, not meant to be taken literally, that expresses something in such a way that it brings the thing to life in the reader's or listener's imagination. [See also *figurative language*.]

flashback   A break in a story's action that relates a past happening in order to give the reader background information about a present action in the story.

folktale   A story that has been passed along from storyteller to storyteller for generations. Kinds of folktales include *tall tales, fairy tales, fables, legends,* and *myths*.

foreshadowing   The use of clues to create suspense by giving the reader or audience hints of events to come.

free verse   Poetry that has no formal rhyme scheme or metrical pattern.

G

genre   A major category of art. The three major literary genres are poetry, prose, and drama.

H

haiku   A three-line Japanese verse form. In most haiku, the first and third lines have five syllables, while the second line has seven. The traditional haiku describes a complicated feeling or thought in simple language through a single image.

hero/heroine   The main character in a work of literature. In heroic literature, the hero or heroine is a particularly brave, noble, or clever person whose achievements are unusual and important. [See also *character*.]

heroic age   The historical period in western civilization—from about 800 B.C. through A.D. 200—during which most works of heroic literature, such as myths and epics, were created in ancient Greece and Rome.

hubris   Arrogance or excessive pride leading to mistakes; the character flaw in a hero of classical tragedy.

hyperbole   An obvious exaggeration used for emphasis. [See also *figurative language*.]

I

idiom   An expression whose meaning cannot be understood from the ordinary meaning of the words. For example, *It's raining cats and dogs*.

imagery   The words and phrases in writing that appeal to the senses of sight, hearing, taste, touch, and smell.

irony An effect created by a sharp contrast between what is expected and what is real. An *ironic twist* in a plot is an event that is the complete opposite of what the characters have been hoping or expecting will happen. An *ironic statement* declares the opposite of the speaker's literal meaning.

J

jargon Words and phrases used by a group of people who share the same profession or special interests in order to refer to technical things or processes with which they are familiar. In general, jargon is any terminology that sounds unclear, overused, or pretentious.

L

legend A famous folktale about heroic actions, passed along by word of mouth from generation to generation. The legend may have begun as a factual account of real people and events but has become mostly or completely fictitious.

limerick A form of light verse, or humorous poetry, written in one five-line stanza with a regular scheme of rhyme and meter.

literature The branch of art that is expressed in written language and includes all written genres.

lyric poem A short poem that expresses personal feelings and thoughts in a musical way. Originally, lyrics were the words of songs that were sung to music played on the lyre, a stringed instrument invented by the ancient Greeks.

M

metamorphosis The transformation of one thing, or being, into another completely different thing or being, such as a caterpillar's change into a butterfly.

metaphor Figurative language in which one thing is said to be another thing. [See also *figurative language*.]

meter The pattern of rhythm in lines of poetry. The most common meter, in poetry written in English, is iambic pentameter, that is, a verse having five metrical feet, each foot of verse having two syllables, an unaccented one followed by an accented one.

mood The feeling or atmosphere that a reader senses while reading or listening to a work of literature.

motivation A character's reasons for doing, thinking, feeling, or saying something. Sometimes an author will make a character's motivation obvious from the beginning. In realistic fiction and drama, however, a character's motivation may be so complicated that the reader discovers it gradually, by studying the character's thoughts, feelings, and behavior.

myth A story, passed along by word of mouth for generations, about the actions of gods and goddesses or superhuman heroes and heroines. Most myths were first told to explain the origins of natural things or to justify the social rules and customs of a particular society.

N

narration The process of telling a story. For both fiction and nonfiction, there are two main kinds of narration, based on whether the story is told from first-person or third-person point of view. [See also *point of view*.]

narrative poem A poem that tells a story containing the basic literary ingredients of fiction: character, setting, and plot.

narrator The person, or voice, that tells a story. [See also *point of view, voice*.]

nonfiction Prose that is factually true and is about real people, events, and places.

nonstandard English
Versions of English, such as slang and dialects, that use pronunciation, vocabulary, idiomatic expressions, grammar, and punctuation that differ from the accepted "correct" constructions of English.

novel   A long work of narrative prose fiction. A novel contains narration, a setting or settings, characters, dialogue, and a more complicated plot than a short story.

O

oral tradition   Stories, poems, and songs that have been kept alive by being told, recited, and sung by people over many generations. Since the works were not originally written, they often have many different versions.

onomatopoeia   The technique of using words that imitate the sounds they describe, such as *hiss, buzz,* and *splash.*

P

parable   A brief story, similar to a fable, but about people, that describes an ordinary situation and concludes with a short moral or lesson to be learned.

personification   Figurative language in which an animal, an object, or an idea is given human characteristics. [See also *figurative language*.]

persuasion   A type of speech or writing whose purpose is to convince people that something is true or important.

play   A work of dramatic literature written for performance by actors before an audience. In classical or traditional drama, a play is divided into five acts, each containing a number of scenes. Each act represents a distinct phase in the development of the plot. Modern plays often have only one act and one scene.

playwright   The author of a play.

plot   The sequence of actions and events in fiction or drama. A traditional plot has at least three parts: the *rising action,* leading up to a turning point that affects the main character; the *climax,* the turning point or moment of greatest intensity or interest; and the *falling action,* leading away from the conflict, or resolving it.

poetry   Language selected and arranged in order to say something in a compressed or nonliteral way. Modern poetry may or may not use many of the traditional poetic techniques that include *meter, rhyme, alliteration, figurative language, symbolism,* and *specific verse forms.*

point of view   The perspective from which a writer tells a story. *First-person* narrators tell the story from their own point of view, using pronouns like *I* or *me. Third-person* narrators, using pronouns like *he, she,* or *them,* may be *omniscient* (knowing everything about all characters), or *limited* (taking the point of view of one character). [See also *narration.*]

propaganda   Information or ideas that may or may not be true, but are spread as though they are true, in order to persuade people to do or believe something.

prose   The ordinary form of written and spoken language used to create fiction, nonfiction, and most drama.

protagonist   The main character of a literary work. [See also *character* and *characterization.*]

R

refrain   A line or group of lines that is repeated, usually at the end of each verse, in a poem or a song.

repetition   The use of the same formal element more than once in a literary work, for emphasis or in order to achieve another desired effect.

resolution   The "falling action" in fiction or drama,

including all of the developments that follow the climax and show that the story's conflict is over. [See also *plot*.]

rhyme scheme   A repeated pattern of similar sounds, usually found at the ends of lines of poetry or poetic drama.

rhythm   In poetry, the measured recurrence of accented and unaccented syllables in a particular pattern. [See also *meter*.]

S

scene   The time, place, and circumstances of a play or a story. In a play, a scene is a section of an act. [See also *play*.]

science fiction   Fantasy literature set in an imaginary future, with details and situations that are designed to seem scientifically possible.

setting   The time and place of a work of literature.

short story   Narrative prose fiction that is shorter and has a less complicated plot than a novel. A short story contains narration, at least one setting, at least one character, and usually some dialogue.

simile   Figurative language that compares two unlike things, introduced by the words "like" or "as." [See also *figurative language*.]

soliloquy   In a play, a short speech spoken by a single character when he or she is alone on the stage. A soliloquy usually expresses the character's innermost thoughts and feelings, when he or she thinks no other characters can hear.

sonnet   A poem written in one stanza, using fourteen lines of iambic pentameter. [See also *meter*.]

speaker   In poetry, the individual whose voice seems to be speaking the lines. [See also *narration, voice*.]

stage directions   The directions, written by the playwright, to tell the director, actors, and theater technicians how a play should be dramatized. Stage directions may specify such things as how the setting should appear in each scene, how the actors should deliver their lines, when the stage curtain should rise and fall, how stage lights should be used, where on the stage the actors should be during the action, and when sound effects should be used.

stanza   A group of lines in poetry set apart by blank lines before and after the group; a poetic verse.

style   The distinctive way in which an author composes a work of literature in written or spoken language.

suspense   An effect created by authors of various types of fiction and drama, especially adventure and mystery plots, to heighten interest in the story.

symbol   An image, person, place, or thing that is used to express the idea of something else.

T

tall tale   A kind of folk tale, or legend, that exaggerates the characteristics of its hero or heroine.

theme   The main idea or underlying subject of a work of literature.

tone   The attitude that a work of literature expresses to the reader through its style.

tragedy   In classical drama, a tragedy depicts a noble hero or heroine who makes a mistake of judgment that has disastrous consequences.

V

verse   A stanza in a poem. Also, a synonym for poetry as a genre. [See also *stanza*.]

voice   The narrator or the person who relates the action of a piece of literature. [See also *speaker*.]

ACKNOWLEDGMENTS

Grateful acknowledgment is made for permission to reprint the following copyrighted material.

"The Marble Champ" by Gary Soto is reprinted from *Baseball in April and Other Stories*. Copyright © 1990 by Gary Soto, by permission of Harcourt Brace & Company.

"Garrett A. Morgan" by Glennette Tilley Turner from *Take a Walk in Their Shoes*. Copyright © 1989 by Glennette Tilley Turner. Used by permission of Cobblehill Books, an affiliate of Dutton Children's Books, a division of Penguin USA, Inc.

from *Nadja on My Way* by Nadja Salerno-Sonnenberg. Copyright © 1989 by Nadja Salerno-Sonnenberg. Reprinted by permission of Crown Publishers.

"Hayes Iverson" and "Lance Perkins" from *Class Dismissed II* by Mel Glenn. Text copyright © 1986 by Mel Glenn. Reprinted by permission of Clarion Books/Houghton Mifflin Co. All rights reserved.

"A Very Special Fighting Machine" by Brent Ashabranner from *People Who Make a Difference*, copyright © 1989 by Brent Ashabranner, text. Copyright © 1989 by Paul Conklin, photographs. Used by permission of Cobblehill Books, an affiliate of Dutton Children's Books, a division of Penguin USA, Inc.

"The Confidence Game" by Pat Carr is reprinted from *Young Miss*, copyright © 1977 by Parent's Magazine Enterprises.

from *There Are No Children Here:* The Story of Two Boys Growing Up in Urban America by Alex Kotlowitz. Copyright © 1991 by Alex Kotlowitz. Used by permission of Doubleday, a division of Bantam Doubleday Dell Publishing Group, Inc.

"Busting Loose" by John Grossmann is reprinted courtesy of *Sports Illustrated For Kids* from the September 1991 issue. Copyright © 1991, Time, Inc. All rights reserved.

"A Personal Narrative" by Kim-Hue Phan is used by permission of the author.

"The Tubeteika Affair" by Vytaute Zilinskaite from *Face to Face:* A Collection of Stories by Celebrated Soviet and American Writers, copyright © 1990 by Thomas Pettepiece and Anatoly Aleskin. Used by permission of Philomel Books, a division of the Putnam and Grosset Book Group.

"To James" by Frank Horne from *Haverstraw*, London, Paul Breman Ltd., 1963. By permission of the publisher.

"Jackie Robinson" by Lucille Clifton from *An Ordinary Woman* by Lucille Clifton, copyright © 1974 by Lucille Clifton. By permission of Curtis Brown, Ltd.

"A Girl Who Would Be Commish" by Mike Fish is reprinted from *The Atlanta Journal* by permission.

"James Ale" from *It's Our World, Too* by Phillip Hoose. Copyright © 1993 by Phillip Hoose. By permission of Little, Brown and Company.

ILLUSTRATION

37 Illustration by Dave Shepherd; 38-45 Border by John Rumery; 66-69, 75 Maps by John Rumery.

PHOTOGRAPHY

4 *l* Carol Palmer/©D.C. Heath; *r* R.M. Collins, III/The Image Works; 6 Harriet Gans/The Image Works; 8-9 Jon Nickson/©D.C. Heath; 10 *t, b* Julie Bidwell/©D.C. Heath; 11 *t* Richard Haynes/©D.C. Heath; *c* Steve & Mary Skjold Photographs; *b* Harriet Gans/The Image Works; 12-19 *t* Jon Nickson/©D.C. Heath; 19 *m* Photo by Carolyn Soto. Courtesy of Harcourt Brace and Co.; *b* Jon Nickson/©D.C. Heath; 20 *inset, l* Culver Pictures, Inc.; *inset, c* Cleveland Public Library; *inset, r,* 20-21, 22 *l, c* Culver Pictures, Inc.; 22 *r* UPI/Bettman; 25 Courtesy of Penguin USA; 26 M.J. Quay. Courtesy of M.L. Falcone; 29 Courtesy of the artist and M.L. Falcone; 32 Stephanie Berger; 36 Focus on Sports; 38-39, 42 Paul Conklin; 45 Jennifer Ashbranner. Courtesy of Penguin USA; 46-53 *t* Courtesy of the artist and Michael Walls Gallery, New York; 53 *b* Peggy Steele; 54-55, 57 *detail*, 58 *detail* Evan-Tibbs Collection, Washington, D.C. Photo: Gary Garrison; 59 Courtesy of David Black Literary Agency, Inc.; 61 Allan Billmeier; 63 Alan Levenson; 65 Mark Seliger; 66 *t* Courtesy of Kim-Hue Phan; *b* Ira Chaplain/Black Star; 73 Courtesy of Kim-Hue Phan; 74-85 Ken O'Donoghue/©D.C. Heath; 86-87 David Madison/Duomo; 88 *tl, tr* Leland's Photo Archive; *ml, m* FPG International; *mr* The Bettman Archive; *bl, br* Leland's Photo Archive; 89 *t* FPG International; *t, inset* Leland's Photo Archive; *m* Courtesy of St. Mary's College of Maryland; *br* FPG International; 90 Marlene Karas/*The Atlanta Journal and Constitution*; 92-93 *inset* *The Miami Herald*/C.M. Guerrero; 92-101 Victor Ramos/©D.C. Heath; 103 Nancy Sheehan/©D.C. Heath; 104 Nancy Sheehan; 106 *b* Ken O'Donoghue/©D.C. Heath; *t* Jeff M. Dunn/Stock Boston; 109 Don & Pat Valenti/Tony Stone Images; 111 David Madison/Tony Stone Images; 112 Elizabeth Crews/Stock Boston; 113 Tony Freeman/Photo Edit; 114 *t* Jeff Greenberg/Photo/Edit; *b* Mary Kate Denny/PhotoEdit.

Back cover *t* Richard Haynes/©D.C. Heath; *c* Julie Bidwell/©D.C. Heath; *b* John Owens/©D.C. Heath.

Full Pronunciation Key for Footnoted Words

(Each pronunciation and definition is adapted from *Scott, Foresman Advanced Dictionary* by E.L. Thorndike and Clarence L. Barnhart.)

The pronunciation of each footnoted word is shown just after the word, in this way: **abbreviate** [ə brē′ vē āt]. The letters and signs used are pronounced as in the words below. The mark ′ is placed after a syllable with primary or heavy accent, as in the example above. The mark ′ after a syllable shows a secondary or lighter accent, as in **abbreviation** [ə brē′ vē ā′ shən].

Some words, taken from foreign languages, are spoken with sounds that do not otherwise occur in English. Symbols for these sounds are given in the key as "foreign sounds."

a	hat, cap	j	jam, enjoy	u	cup, butter	**foreign sounds**
ā	age, face	k	kind, seek	ù	full, put	Y as in French *du*.
ä	father, far	l	land, coal	ü	rule, move	Pronounce (ē) with
		m	me, am	v	very, save	the lips rounded as
b	bad, rob	n	no, in	w	will, woman	for (ü).
ch	child, much	ng	long, bring	y	young, yet	
d	did, red			z	zero, breeze	à as in French *ami*.
		o	hot, rock	zh	measure, seizure	Pronounce (ä) with
e	let, best	ō	open, go			the lips spread and
ē	equal, be	ô	order, all	ə represents:		held tense.
ėr	term, learn	oi	oil, voice		a in about	
		ou	house, out		e in taken	œ as in French *peu*.
f	fat, if				i in pencil	Pronounce (ā) with the
g	go, bag	p	paper, cup		o in lemon	lips rounded as for (ō).
h	he, how	r	run, try		u in circus	
		s	say, yes			N as in French *bon*.
i	it, pin	sh	she, rush			The N is not pro-
ī	ice, five	t	tell, it			nounced, but shows
		th	thin, both			that the vowel before
		₮H	then, smooth			it is nasal.

H as in German *ach*. Pronounce (k) without closing the breath passage.